AMERICA READS SPANISH
www.americareadsspanish.org

THE NEW
ESSENTIAL GUIDE
TO SPANISH READING

Librarians' Selections

AMERICA READS SPANISH
www.americareadsspanish.org

THE NEW ESSENTIAL GUIDE TO SPANISH READING: Librarian's Selections

Some of the contributors to this New Essential Guide to Spanish Reading appeared on the original guide. We have maintained some of their reviews, keeping the original comment and library at the time.

ISBN 13: 978-0-9828388-7-7

Edited by Lluís Agustí and Fundación Germán Sánchez Ruipérez
Translated by Eduardo de Lamadrid
Revised by Alina San Juan

Sponsored by:

This is a non commercial edition and is not for sale.
For free copies of this book, contact the Trade Commission of Spain in Miami at:

TRADE COMMISSION OF SPAIN
2655 LeJeune Rd, Suite 1114
CORAL GABLES, FL 33134
Tel. (305) 446-4387
e-mail: miami@mcx.es
www.americareadsspanish.org

America Reads Spanish is the name of the campaign sponsored by the Spanish Institute for Foreign Trade and the Spanish Association of Publishers Guilds, whose purpose is to increase the reading and use of Spanish through the auspices of thousands of libraries, schools and booksellers in the United States.

Printed in the United States of America

GENERAL INDEX

▶ INTRODUCTIONS   Pg.   7

▶ CATEGORY INDEX   Pg. 15

▶ AUTHORS INDEX   Pg. 197

▶ TITLES INDEX   Pg. 233

▶ COLLABORATORS INDEX   Pg. 253

▶ NOTES   Pg. 257

INTRODUCTIONS

INTRODUCTIONS

Dear Friends,

It gives me great pleasure to present the New Essential Guide to Spanish Reading, brought to fruition with the support of ICEX, CEDRO, FGEE and the Germán Sánchez Ruipérez Foundation.

As a publisher, I have frequently asked myself about the scope of the works we bring to market. Determining the size of print runs is more often than not a thorny question. If the print run is too large, it may penalize investment in new titles, if it is too small, then the disruption in stocks could negatively affect sales and space allocation in bookstores. The digital format may lesson the uncertainties we harbor in regard to printed works, but it does not allay our anxiety about the scope of a work to be published. Certainly, a work originating in Spain for a Spanish readership that transcends our borders and captures the North American market is a source of pride for the publisher and the author. It is not merely a financial matter, but also a source of professional pride. In this sense, for some years now Spanish publishers have achieved a certain degree of penetration in the North American market, thanks to an increasing Spanish-speaking population and to students of the language, often animated to do so by campaigns like America Reads Spanish.

The LIBER International Book Fair, alternatively hosted by Barcelona and Madrid, has given us the opportunity to meet visiting North American librarians and distributors, who are consummate professionals. This contact among professionals is crucial for gathering first-hand information about what new books are simmering in the Spanish publishing world and for recommendation for additions to North American libraries. Likewise, the American librarians and distributors who visit LIBER know what their reading publics demand. In this way, North American demand is matched to the supply offered by Spanish publishers.

INTRODUCTIONS

We hope that the selection of over six hundred basic titles in this new edition will animate youngsters of all ages to join the book reading world, key for any society committed to the youth-book binomial, and essential for achieving greater levels of liberty and culture. Reading and books will ensure that the many new immigrants to the United States have a bridge between liberty and culture, a goal proven very difficult to reach by other means.

From a business perspective, it is very stimulating to have a presence in the United States market, in which competitiveness and quality take precedence over other parameters. Spanish publishers are pleased to take on the challenges of this market, as we have done in our own natural markets for a great number of years, and in so doing, have been recompensed by the creation of a great publishing industry in Spain.

Finally, we cannot overstate the invaluable cooperation of the Germán Sánchez Ruipérez Foundation, whose enthusiasm for, and knowledge of, the world of books for children and young adults, has decisively contributed to the edition of this selection of books we are now presenting.

We hope that our efforts to produce this second edition prove to be interesting and gratifying to you, and help to deepen the bonds between our cultures.

Antoni Comas
Spanish Association of Publishers Guilds

INTRODUCTIONS

It is with great pleasure that I introduce this second edition of the Essential Guide to Spanish Reading, a revised and improved volume that gathers the best commentaries and reviews of professionals in the industry, who understand the need for such a tool. This Guide is meant for librarians to enhance the Spanish book collections in their libraries.

This Guide has been elaborated as part of the promotional plan America Reads Spanish with the support of the Spanish Institute for Foreign Trade, with the aim to attend the increasing demand for Spanish language materials in the U.S.

Currently, there are more Spanish speaking people in the U.S. than there is in Spain, which explains the more than 30,000 Guides we have distributed during the last four years, helping to increase and improve librarians and book sellers' offer to their communities.

Our objective is to contribute to the promotion of reading in Spanish as a step in the process of positioning Spanish culture and commerce in the United States, since both language and understanding are main objectives towards a successful exchange of ideas and projects between our two countries.

After the success of the first edition of this Guide, of which we are deeply proud, we continued working on this project, culminating in the presentation of this new edition, with 640 titles, which includes a more extensive section for children and young adults.

Mª Coriseo González-Izquierdo
Consejera Delegada del ICEX

INTRODUCTIONS

The best and/or most informative Spanish books on the subjects of Fiction and Literature; Poetry and Drama; Non-Fiction, Reference and Children and Young Adults are described in this New Essential Guide to Spanish Reading a bibliography for professionals, scholars, students, and lay people. The informative abstracts, including titles new to this edition, range in length from 50 to 100 words for more than 600 titles in Spanish, and have been written by professional journalists, teachers, booksellers and librarians that work with Latino communities in the United States.

I commend America Reads Spanish that once again took the challenge and worked hard to launch this New Essential Guide to Spanish Reading. Now that Latinos are 16.3% of the US population surpassing all other minority groups, I am very sure that the New Essential Guide to Spanish Reading will be in all U.S. libraries providing services to our 50.5 million people called Latinos.

Maria Kramer
REFORMA President 2011-12

INTRODUCTIONS

▶ A NOTE FROM AMERICA READS SPANISH. ◀

▶ The Risks of a Plural Endeavor.

The open, one might say, choral, nature of this bibliography stems from its own genesis; this is not simply a conventional determination of a canon, rather its value and its richness reside in the fact that the recommended works have been previously read, consulted and used by the professionals who suggested them and who so aver.

The procedure for obtaining the titles in this New Guide was undoubtedly a risky proposition; precedence was given to free participation over the normative pyramidal process involving literary editors, the distribution of areas of expertise, etc., knowing all the while of the possible disparity in authors, themes, eras and geographic areas which might thus obtain.

The final result presented now demonstrates that it was worth assuming that risk. The New Guide is a rich and plural, distinctive bibliography, and while many of the names listed therein are found in the canons of the most representative works of our literatures, in other instances one will find lesser known or forgotten authors and works, but which nonetheless are of equal import and interest.

▶ Structure of the New Guide.

The bibliography is divided into five major sections: Literature and Fiction, Poetry and Drama, Non Fiction, Reference Works, and Children and Young Adult Literature. In each section, the works are ordered alphabetically by title. Each reference includes the title in Spanish, a brief note about the work, and the name of

INTRODUCTIONS

the author of the comment and his or her profession and/or institution. It was deemed appropriate not to include information relative to places of publication, publishers, collections, and ISBNs. The New Guide is further supplemented by general indexes by authors, titles and collaborators.

▶ **Usefulness of the New Guide.**

The New Guide aspires to be useful for librarians who wish to endow a basic Hispanic corpus or to complete the one they currently possess with quality works. It may also prove valuable for American booksellers who wish to enrich their offerings for a more demanding readership. Undoubtedly, the New Guide may also provide practical support in the selection of works for teachers and professors of Spanish and Hispanic literatures. Finally, the New Guide may be used by any reader who seeks advice or suggestions.

CATEGORY INDEX

▶ LITERATURE / FICTION   Pg. 17

▶ NON FICTION   Pg. 95

▶ POETRY / DRAMA   Pg. 121

▶ REFERENCE   Pg. 143

▶ CHILDREN / YOUNG ADULTS   Pg. 157

LITERATURE
FICTION

2666.

Author: Roberto Bolaño

The five novels which comprise this monumental work have a common leitmotif based on a historical event: the murders of the women of Juárez. An astonishing display of audacity and narrative power, 2666 blends the structures and essences of the best in European and American narrative, putting itself forward as a new and revolutionary modality of the total novel, which combines traits both of the detective story and the epic poem.

▶ *Juan Pablo Debesis*   Lectorum

A LA DERIVA Y OTROS CUENTOS.

Author: Horacio Quiroga

A collection of short stories by one of Uruguay's finest writers.

▶ *Scott Van Jacob*   University of Notre Dame

A QUIEN CORRESPONDA.

Author: Walter Ventosilla

NEW

To Whom It May Concern is a collection of startling short stories, all set in big cities save one, which takes place in a Peruvian village in the Andes. All stories relate with the experiences of the narrator who bares his immigrant spirit in each tale. This book presents the reality of many who have dared to cross borders legally or illegally. Survival, the achievement of dreams, and social and human obstacles become everyday battles that must be faced by those who decided to change their life but not their spirit.

▶ *Scott Van Jacob*   University of Notre Dame

ABRIL ROJO.

Author: Santiago Roncagliolo

NEW

This novel revisits a classic detective novel plot in which the investigator, not satisfied with the police version of the case, decides to inquire beyond official police procedures, and stirs the stagnant waters until he finds the real truth. In this case, he is a district attorney posted to a small Peruvian town, and the price he will pay will be to come face to face with horror itself. With a formidable style, the author recreates popular speech in fast-moving dialogues, while delving into the human character and the circumstances of the country.

▶ *Paloma Graciani*   Biblioteca "José Emilio Pacheco"

ADIÓS HEMINGWAY.

Author: Leonardo Padura

Mystery readers and Hemingway fans alike will enjoy the latest case of Padura's postmodern detective Mario Conde. Skeletal remains found in Hemingway's Cuban home require an investigation that leads to revelations about the author's final years.

▶   *Teresa Chapa*   University of North Carolina at Chapel Hill

ADIRE y el TIEMPO ROTO.

Author: Manuel Granados

The most important Cuban novel written by a black author, its poetic language captivated José Lezama Lima and dazzled Julio Cortázar. One of the great forgotten works of Cuban literature, which again is being discovered by new generations of readers.

▶   *Fernando Velázquez Medina*   Writer and Journalist

EL ALEPH.

Author: Jorge Luis Borges

Among the unparalleled volumes of stories by Borges, perhaps none is as well-known as this one. The title story is probably the most discussed and analyzed narrative in Latin American literature.

▶   *Octavio Núñez*   US Librarian

ALGUNAS NUBES.

Author: Paco Taibo II
NEW

Mexico City F.D. is the setting for this violent story which presents a mordant critique of the Mexican police machine as well as detailed descriptions of the grosteque characters that inhabit that world. This is the third in a series of novels featuring the best known detective in Mexican literature, Hector Belascoaran Shayn, and is peppered with the intrigues of corrupt power centers and touches of humor.

▶   *Paloma Graciani*   Biblioteca "José Emilio Pacheco"

EL ALQUIMISTA IMPACIENTE.

Author: Lorenzo Silva

NEW

This is an essential novel for lovers of the crime genre, written by one of the great names of the modern Spanish detective thriller.

▶ *Paloma Graciani*   Biblioteca "José Emilio Pacheco"

 ## EL AMOR EN LOS TIEMPOS DEL CÓLERA.

Author: Gabriel García Márquez

This is my favorite of García Márquez's novels. In his magical style he follows the obsessive love of Florentino for Fermina and after 50 years we all rejoice in the happy reunion and love of the pair.

▶ *Millie Torrance*   Sacramento Public Library

 ## LA AMORTAJADA.

Author: María Luisa Bombal

One of the most outstanding works in Latin American literature written by a woman, both intimate and fantastic in nature, is still required reading and study in literature programs.

▶ *Octavio Núñez*   US Librarian

 ## ANTES QUE ANOCHEZCA: AUTOBIOGRAFÍA.

Author: Reinaldo Arenas

Profoundly human and intensely political award-winning memoir recounts the author's incredible journey from a childhood of poverty in Cuba to his imprisonment for homosexuality, his suppression as a writer and his life in the U.S.

▶ *Patricia Cuesta*   Los Angeles Public Library

ANTOLOGÍA PERSONAL.

Author: Julio Ramón Ribeyro

The intimate relationship between the author and tobacco is analyzed with both humor and fatalism in "For Smokers Only", the first selection in this compilation from the master of the short story. It also includes essays, plays and diary entries.

▶ *Richard Heyer*   Instituto Cervantes New York

APRENDICES DE BRUJO.

Author: Antonio Orlando Rodríguez

NEW

This novel, set in the Roaring Twenties, is thematically unique. Mixing satire with urban adventure, high society with the demimonde, it very successfully recreates the atmosphere of the age. An unforgettable reading experience.

▶ *Robert Zaman*   US Librarian

EL ÁRBOL DE LA CIENCIA.

Author: Pío Baroja

The Tree of Knowledge belongs to Pío Baroja's trilogy called The Race (La Raza). This novel about education and reflection on the human condition became an instant classic within the Spanish literary tradition and especially as a psychological work for speculations by the young. It relates the life of Andrés Hurtado, medical student and later village doctor and researcher, a life which is not self-explanatory, which does not have a meaning or absolute reasons to justify it, and in which knowledge and responsibilities are not sources of pleasure but of pain.

▶ *Lluís Agustí*   Instituto Cervantes New York

ARRÁNCAME LA VIDA.

Author: Angeles Mastretta

If the title sounds like a bolero, it's because the narrative carries the story of a strong woman in post-revolutionary Mexico with such melodic text. And indeed, the English edition was published as Mexican Bolero in 1989.

▶ *Adan Griego*   Stanford University Libraries

EL ASCO: THOMAS BERNHARD EN EL SALVADOR.

 Author: Horacio Castellanos Moya

Each country should engender a writer who has the capacity of devastating the reader on the page. In the case of El Salvador, Castellanos Moya is that man. In a bitter but brilliant exercise, the protagonist of the book implacably explodes symbols, institutions, characters and everything which constitutes the internal and external life of a country, without distinction to political allegiance or social class. Disgust (El Asco) is also an exercise in style, an intelligent bomb of acerbic humor. In his fierce but lucid fall, the protagonist will come to the end of himself, understanding that although granted exile, forgetting is denied to him. With novels like Arms in the Man (El Arma en el Hombre) and Dance with Serpents (Baile con Serpientes), written in agile and steely prose, Castellanos Moya is without a doubt one of the best and most intense Central American and Hispanic American writers of our times.

▶ *Gaspar Orozco*   Mexican Poet and Diplomat

EL ASEDIO.

 Author: Arturo Pérez-Reverte   **NEW**

El asedio takes place in Cádiz during the Spanish War of Independence in 1811 and 1812. While Spain is occupied by the French army and fights for its freedom, Cádiz is witnessing a different kind of massacre. Women's bodies are found throughout the city in strategic places, mimicking a chess board. El asedio is not a proper historical or war novel like Cabo Trafalgar or Un día de cólera by the same author, but rather a complex thriller featuring a corrupt policeman, the heiress of a powerful local family, a sea captain, a taxidermist, a guerilla fighter from the salt marshes and an eccentric artilleryman. In this crime novel the laws of probability and precise calculations based on mathematics and physics are key to the outcome of the story.

▶ *Patricia Figueroa*   Brown University

ASESINATO EN EL COMITÉ CENTRAL.

 Author: Manuel Vázquez Montalbán   **NEW**

Pepe Carvalho is the Hispanic equivalent of the great misanthropic and skeptical detectives which abound in the American thriller. In this case, the detective has to investigate the death of Secretary General of the Communist Party of Spain, assassinated while presiding over a meeting of the Party's Central Committee.

▶ *Paloma Graciani*   Biblioteca "José Emilio Pacheco"

EL ASTILLERO.

 Author: Juan Carlos Onetti
NEW

Without a doubt, Onetti is one of the greatest writers of Uruguayan letters. Creator of dark and oppressive settings, Onetti sets this story in Santa María, locale where his other novels take place. Larsen, the protagonist, returns after long years of exile with the idea of managing an old shipyard, but finds it to be as decrepit as everything else that surrounds him. Juan Carlos Onetti was awarded the Cervantes Prize in 1980.

▶ *Salvador Vergara*   Instituto Cervantes Chicago

AVENTURAS LITERARIAS.

 Author: Ana C. Jarvis, Raquel Lebredo, and Francisco Mena-Ayllón

This book contains short stories written by Latinamerican and Spaniards authors. It also contains classical poetry (Amado Nervo).

▶ *Guillermina Raffo Magnasco*   St. Thomas University

AVES SIN NIDO.

 Author: Clorinda Matto de Turner
NEW

The feudal social system in the Andean village of "Killac" is upset when an educated couple from Lima move into the area. When they try to help a local Indian family, Lucía and Fernando Marín become involved in a violent conflict with the political and religious authorities of the town.

▶ *Richard Heyer*   Biblioteca "Jorge Luis Borges"

BALAS DE PLATA.

 Author: Elmer Mendoza
NEW

Élmer Mendoza presents a novel which has all the requirements of the crime fiction genre: a detective, a murder, a list of suspects, a corrupt milieu, and an ending which is symptomatic of a skeptical take on Mexican reality. Vengeance, not the law, is the victor. This is an excellent example of what critics have dubbed narcoliterature.

▶ *Paloma Graciani*   Biblioteca "José Emilio Pacheco"

BALÚN CANÁN.

Author: Rosario Castellanos

A coming-of-age story about a young girl's life on a Chiapas coffee plantation, by the Mexican novelist, poet and diplomat.

▶ *Lynn Shirey*   Harvard College Library

BARRIO DE MARAVILLAS.

Author: Rosa Chacel

In my opinion, this is the greatest novel of 20th century Spanish literature, much more important for the style of its telling and how it provides glimpses of the author's mind than for what it tells. Inward-looking, following the aesthetic theories of Ortega y Gasset, its narrative techniques preceded the French nouveau roman by many years.

▶ *Juan Carlos Vidal*   Instituto Cervantes Chicago

LAS BATALLAS DEL DESIERTO.

Author: José Emilio Pacheco

A minimalist gem from Mexican writer José Emilio Pacheco.

▶ *Juan Carlos Vidal*   Instituto Cervantes Chicago

BENDÍCEME, ÚLTIMA.

Author: Rudolfo Anaya

Award-winning, uniquely North American coming-of-age novel chronicles the story of an alienated young man in New Mexico who seeks answers to questions about the meaning of life from the magical healer, Última.

▶ *Patricia Cuesta*   Los Angeles Public Library

EL BESO DE LA MUJER ARAÑA.

Author: Manuel Puig

Written within an unusual structure in which there is no narrator and where dialogue takes up most of the text, this is an indispensable novel of Latin American literature. It narrates the story of two prisoners who cohabit the same cell, one a political dissident and the other a homosexual, and of the friendship that slowly develops between them.

▶ *Octavio Núñez* US Librarian

BEST OF CONTEMPORARY MEXICAN FICTION.

Authors: Alvaro Uribe y Olivia Sears

NEW

Sixteen of Mexico's finest fiction writers born after 1945 are collected in this bilingual anthology. Mexican editor Alvaro Uribe selected prominent editors, translators, columnists, professors and the young founder of a new publishing collective. Together they have received dozens of literary prizes. Contents range from small-town drama to tales of urban savagery with most stories and writers appearing in English for the first time.

▶ *Nancy Klasterka* Hoover Public Library

BESTIARIO.

Author: Juan José Arreola

This is probably the best short story collection by one of the great masters of the Latin American short story. After publication, its author immediately became a name to be reckoned with in the short story telling genre of the South American continent.

▶ *Octavio Núñez* US Librarian

BOMARZO.

Author: Manuel Mujica Lainez

In my opinion, this is one of the best novels written in Latin America. This historical novel captures the spirit of the Italian Renaissance through its depiction of the Orsini family. It expertly blends history with a rarefied atmosphere of fantasy. This text is universal and can be counted among the best historical novels in all literature.

▶ *Robert Zaman* US Librarian

BUENAS NOCHES A TODOS.

Author: Sergio Gómez

An excellent short story collection. A very Chilean milieu and yet the experiences of every day characters explore very universal themes.

▶ *Adan Griego*   Stanford University

EN BUSCA DEL UNICORNIO.

Author: Juan Eslava Galán

King Henry IV of Castile, called the Impotent, needs help to ensure that his lineage will keep the throne. To accomplish this, he sends one of his best knights, Juan de Olid, in search of a unicorn's horn, in the hope that the horn's aphrodisiac effects will help the monarch with his task. The knight departs for the heart of Africa in search of the mythical animal accompanied by a small and unique contingent which include a friar and a virgin girl, who, according to legend, must be offered in order to attract the elusive animal. A hilarious and entertaining parody of historical and adventure novels.

▶ *Lluís Agustí*   Instituto Cervantes New York

CABALLO DE TROYA.

Author: J.J. Benítez

A novel written about the last weeks in the life of Jesus Christ and about time travel. A series that delves into religious conspiracy theories, especially popular in today's culture.

▶ *Angela Encinas*   San Bernardino Public Library

CAFÉ HUGO.

Author: Adolfo García Ortega

Alleghorical novel that takes place on one extraordinary and sleepless night – March 7, 1966 – in the microcosmos of Café Hugo, point of convergence in an unidentified city in an unidentified province of Spain. Award-winning Spanish novelist Adolfo García Ortega is also a renowned translator, literary critic, journalist, and book editor.

▶ *Claude Potts*   University of California

CAFÉ NOSTALGIA.

 Author: Zoe Valdés

The author illustrates what it feels to be exiled. Not only from one's country but from one's life.

▶ *Angela Encinas*   San Bernardino Public Library

CAÍN.

 Author: José Saramago

NEW

The story follows Cain as God sends him on his peripatetic way after having murdered Abel. The narrator places Cain at Old Testament hotspots - Abraham deciding to sacrifice his son, in bed with Lilith, working for Job, at the tower of Babel, Sodom and Gomorrah and on Noah's ark. God does not come out smelling like a rose from this point of view.

▶ *Sara Martínez*   Tulsa City-County Library

CARAMELO: PURO CUENTO.

 Author: Sandra Cisneros

Inspirational novel by an acclaimed Mexican-American author provides insight into a multigenerational working-class migrant Mexican family as told through the eyes of granddaughter Lala.

▶ *Patricia Cuesta*   Los Angeles Public Library

LA CARNE DE RENÉ.

 Author: Virgilio Piñera

"Flesh desires flesh, and the soul seeks its own like," reads a line by the 15th-century poet Ausiàs March. René's Flesh is one of the best-known novels by the renowned Cuban play-wright Virgilio Piñera. This fascinating bildungsroman unfolds by using the body as a way to learn via the flesh.

▶ *Lluís Agustí*   Instituto Cervantes New York

EL CARTERO DE NERUDA: ARDIENTE PACIENCIA

 Author: Antonio Skármeta

Chilean writer Antonio Skármeta depicts in his novel Burning Patience, later put into screen to a successful movie, The Postman, the friendship between Chile's national poet and Nobel Laureate Pablo Neruda, exiled on Isla Negra, with Mario Jiménez, a young postman whose only duty is to deliver the famous author's mail. Skármeta sets the story during President Salvador Allende's administration drawing parallels between Mario's private life and romantic involvement with beautiful Beatriz, and the public turbulence and violence that gradually overtakes Chile.

▶ *Libbhy Romero*   Brooklyn Public Library

CARTUCHO: RELATOS DE LA LUCHA EN EL NORTE DE MÉXICO

 Author: Nellie Campobello
NEW

A classic narrative of the Mexican Revolution written by the only woman writer of the period. Originally published in 1931, it describes the carnage of war as experienced by a young girl. This annotated edition provides historical and literary analysis lacking in previous editions and complements the 1988 English translation.

▶ *Adan Griego*   Stanford University

LA CASA DE LA LAGUNA.

 Author: Rosario Ferré

A family saga set in Puerto Rico and mirroring passions and events through generations of a family and in Puerto Rico. It was nominated for Premio Nacional del Libro in 1995.

▶ *Millie Torrance*   Sacramento Public Library

LA CASA DE LOS ESPÍRITUS.

 Author: Isabel Allende

The House of the Spirits is in my opinion Allende's most famous and important book. The multi-generational story of the Trueba family is used to weave an intricate tale of Chilean history, from the early turn of the century through the upheaval and revolution of the 70's.

▶ *Miriam Rodríguez*   Dallas Public Library

LA CATEDRAL DEL MAR.

Author: Ildefonso Falcones

The most successful new work in Spain in 2006.

▶ *Julio Rivas*   Reader

CAYO CANAS.

Author: Lino Novás Calvo

A collection of stories which incorporate the most novel techniques of North American storytelling, as assimilated by this Cuban author born in Galicia, Spain. Displaying great linguistic, stylistic and compositional innovations, this collection placed Novás Calvo at the forefront of Latin American literature.

▶ *Fernando Velázquez Medina*   Writer and Journalist

CENIZAS DEL QUERER.

Author: Emilia Pereyra

Pereyra's second novel transports us to Azua, a small province in southern Dominican Republic, where we discover the complex and false world of Doña Beatriz. In this magical space, where individuals must define themselves, Doña Beatriz encounters social prejudice and endures the moral norms in her rural surroundings.

▶ *Nashieli Marcano*   University of Akron

LOS CENTROAMERICANOS: ANTOLOGÍA DE CUENTOS.

Author: José Mejía, ed.

An excellent selection of best short fiction of Central America. A geographic and personal tour consciously effected by some of the best contemporary short stories in some of the more unknown national literatures in Spanish.

▶ *Lluís Agustí*   Instituto Cervantes New York

LA CHARCA.

Author: Manuel Zeno Gandía

This bitter melodrama tells a story about plantation workers' struggle for survival in Puerto Rico in the late 19th century. The beautiful island countryside, contrasted with the starved and diseased human beings who live there, makes this "naturalista" work a classic in Puerto Rican literature.

▶ *Nashieli Marcano*   University of Akron

EL CHICO DE ORO.

Author: Michael Nava

Nava is one of the great gay Chicano writers. El chico de oro was his first novel and introduced us to a gay Chicano detective (Henry Rios) who moved through the California landscape crossing the borders of class and sexuality. Henry Rios appeared in several other mystery novels by Nava. To date, this is the only in Spanish and it deserves a much wider audience.

▶ *Adan Griego*   Stanford University Libraries

CHIQUITA.

Author: Antonio Orlando Rodríguez
                                                     NEW

Winner of the Alfaguara Prize for the Novel in 2008, this novel takes inspiration of a real life female midget, who was born in provincial Cuba and reached the stages of New York in the 19th century and became a star, only to later disappear mysteriously. An excellent exercise of style and well-captured atmosphere.

▶ *Octavio Núñez*   US Librarian

CIEN AÑOS DE SOLEDAD.

Author: Gabriel García Márquez

Anyone interested in learning about Latin American culture must read this book, certainly a literary masterpiece. Macondo is the name of the world created by García Márquez which we can compare with many towns around Latin America. The magical realism of his characters makes us feel as if we were members of the Buendía's family. The 1982 nobel prize winner can make one read this book several times, and there will always be someting new that was overlooked before. The descriptions of feelings of his caracters are detailed to the point that we will love, hate and suffer along with them. CIEN AÑOS DE SOLEDAD is absolutely a must-read book.

▶ *Yeni Lizarraga*   Adler's Foreign Books INC.

CINCO HORAS CON MARIO.

Author: Miguel Delibes

It's the mid-60's in Spain, Mario has just died. Menchu, his wife, keeps vigil over the corpse as she recalls in a vibrant and disordered monologue diverse stories and anecdotes of their life in common. From Menchu's reflections, the figure of Mario takes shape —his way of life, his hobbies, his desires, his ideals which stand in stark contrast to those of Spain during the 25 Years of Peace— as well as her own. This impeccable tapestry of memories has been written in such a way that it has been adapted to theater as a monologue.

▷ *Lluís Agustí*   Instituto Cervantes New York

CINCO MAESTROS: Cuentos modernos de Hispanoamérica.

Author: Alexander Coleman

These are short stories from five Latin American authors. The book contains a bilingual vocabulary, which is an enrichment resource for American students.

▷ *Guillermina Raffo Magnasco*   St. Thomas University

LOS CIPRESES CREEN EN DIOS.

Author: José María Gironella

When I read it, I was a student in Spain in the year 1978 or 1979. It impressed me so much that every night I dreamt that I was one character or another from the book. Gironella provides the reader not only an understanding, but also a knowledge, an authentic flavor, as it were, of the Spanish Civil War of 1936-1939.

▷ *Mark Pendleton*   Branigan Library Las Cruces NM

LA CIUDAD DE LOS PRODIGIOS.

Author: Eduardo Mendoza

Onofre Bouvila, a poor peasant, arrives in Barcelona to work in the World Exhibition of 1888. The story of Bouvila's acquisition of wealth and social ascent, not always in an orthodox manner, runs in parallel to the development of the city of wonder until another key event, the International Exhibition of 1929. One of the best novels written about stirring, turn of the century Barcelona.

▷ *Lluís Agustí*   Instituto Cervantes New York

LA CIUDAD y los PERROS.

 Author: Mario Vargas Llosa

I was fifteen years old when I read The City and the Dogs, Vargas Llosa's first novel. It was my first encounter with great literature and I was dazzled. Silently following the jaguar, the slave and Alberto, I discovered a new and fascinating world, and I decided that I wanted to be a reader.

▶ *Santiago Cabanas*   Cónsul General de España en Miami

EL CLUB DUMAS.

 Author: Arturo Pérez-Reverte

This is the perfect detective story for a bibliophile. The intrigue involves a rare book detective in search of a banned seventeenth century manuscript of the occult.

▶ *Teresa Chapa*   University of North Carolina at Chapel Hill

LA COLMENA.

 Author: Camilo José Cela

Set in the cafes of Madrid and boasting a legion of characters, La colmena is a choral novel which masterfully describes the misery of the immediate aftermath of the Civil War. The characters survive hunger, the economic and moral strictures, and above all, the lack of hope, in a sordid and gray atmosphere.

▶ *Lluís Agustí*   Instituto Cervantes New York

EL COLOR del VERANO.

NEW

Author: Reinaldo Arenas

El color del verano is a Rabelaisian masterpiece written by Arenas as he lay dying from complications from AIDS in a hospital bed. It's an experimental novel, a series of vignettes and a roman-a-clef that tells the story in the uncompromising language of Reinaldo's youth and his friends, a lost generation of gays that suffer under the despotic rule of Fifo, a dictator who hates everything that is beautiful, genuine and spontaneous in life. It contains a 50 page poem of rhymed couplets and prose which at its best is magisterial.

▶ *Radamés Suárez*   Queens Library

COMO AGUA PARA CHOCOLATE.

 Author: Laura Esquivel

Another classic of Latin American women's literature, this novel is considered to be the author's magnum opus. This story, seasoned with recipes of great culinary and literary value, was made into a very successful film.

▶ *Octavio Núñez*   US Librarian

CONDENADOS DE CONDADO.

 Author: Norberto Fuentes

This collection of stories won the Casa de Americas prize in 1968, awarded by a jury chaired by Jorge Edwards. Published in Italy with a prologue by Italo Calvino, the collection evinces a happy amalgam of the styles of Hemingway and Babel. A Cuban short story classic.

▶ *Fernando Velázquez Medina*   Writer and Journalist

CONSPIRACIÓN MAINE.

 Author: Mario Escobar Golderos

Conspiración Maine is a very interesting historical thriller about the sinking of the battleship Maine in the port of Havana in February 1898. It convincingly depicts U.S. aspirations for political dominance, as well as the old Spanish empire in the throes of decadence. Two secret agents, a young female reporter and a professor, will have to discover what's behind the sinking of the ship. A secret organization called the Knights of Columbus stands in their way. A true adventure story full of surprising twists and an exciting ending.

▶ *Angel Santiago Cervantes*   Cahesa

CONVERSACIÓN EN LA CATEDRAL.

 Author: Mario Vargas Llosa

Cited by many as one of best structured novels of Hispanic American literature, this has become a classic and required reading, included in study and thesis programs at dozens of universities.

▶ *Octavio Núñez*   US Librarian

EL CORAZÓN DEL TÁRTARO.

 Author: Rosa Montero

Zarza awakens, on an ordinary, routine day, in her lowly home, to a phone call. That call returns her to her former life, to the center of the inferno, in a 24 hour race that doesn't allow us to leave the book until we have traversed the entire history of Zarza's hellish past.

▶ *Martha Berman*   Professor of Language and Literature

CORAZÓN TAN BLANCO.

 Author: Javier Marías   NEW

Part of "los novísimos" (the very newest) or the generation of 1968, Javier Marías, like his contemporaries, breaks free from the realist and social realist tendencies that dominated Spanish literature for most of the century. Corazón tan blanco is his seventh novel and arguably one of his best. Narrated through the voice of Juan Ranz, this post-existential suspenseful novel transports us to Havana, Madrid, Geneva, and New York as the protagonist investigates his past and questions the meaning of his very existence.

▶ *Claude Potts*   University of California

CORONA DE SOMBRA.

 Author: Rodolfo Usigli   NEW

One of a trilogy of plays written to demythologize key moments in Mexican history, "Corona de sombra" deals with the tragic period of imperial rule by Maximilian and Carlota, European royalty who are presented as benign but completely misguided in their attempts to govern a country about which they knew almost nothing.

▶ *Richard Heyer*   Biblioteca "Jorge Luis Borges"

EL CORONEL NO TIENE QUIEN LE ESCRIBA.

 Author: Gabriel García Márquez

The second novel of the Colombian Nobel prize winner narrates the vain hopes of a Colonel, who every Friday awaits an official letter in reply to his justified claim for a pension. The internal tension of the novel arises from the juxtaposition of minutely described daily miseries and the stoical optimism of the main character.

▶ *Juan Pablo Debesis*   Lectorum

CORTOS.

Author: Alberto Fuguet

In this collection of stories, the Chilean writer Alberto Fuguet accomplished one thing: making clear that one of the unmistakable signs of young Hispanic-American generations is the desire for flight, the wish to disappear. Notoriously watering in the cinema and American pop culture, the Chilean writer reproduces its language, its situations and its mannerisms, as well as in the more fortunate cases, a certain unpredictable character. With its fleeting subject matter, Shorts (Cortos) should be read today, right now, because it's possible that the world it describes might disappear tomorrow.

▶ *Gaspar Orozco*   Mexican Poet and Diplomat

CRISTO versus ARIZONA.

Author: Camilo José Cela

NEW

Published one year before Spanish novelist Camilo José Cela received the Nobel Prize in Literature, this lesser known work is set in the gunslinging and lawless desert of Arizona circa 1881. Without employing a single period or delineation of a paragraph, Cela paints a dreary portrait of man's condition through the uneducated voice of Wendell L. Espana. The novel makes use of a literary style used by Cela known as objectivismo, a kind of documentary realism introduced in earlier masterpieces such as La familia de Pascual Duarte (The Family of Pascual Duarte, 1942) and La colmena (The Hive, 1951).

▶ *Claude Potts*   University of California

CRÓNICA SENTIMENTAL en ROJO.

Author: Francisco González Ledesma

NEW

This is a sarcastic and hard novel, endowed with both elegant cruelty and unforgettable tenderness. Set at the start of the 80s when Spain is undergoing major transitional changes. In that context, old Detective Inspector Méndez becomes involved in a story whose roots dig down into the entrails of the city of Barcelona.

▶ *Paloma Graciani*   Biblioteca "José Emilio Pacheco"

EL CUARTO DE ATRÁS.

Author: Carmen Martín Gaite

An oneiric novel that examines the process of writing fiction.

▶ *Lynn Shirey*   Harvard College Library

EL CUENTO HISPÁNICO: A GRADED LITERARY ANTHOLOGY.

Author: Edward J. Mullen, and John E. Garganigo.

These short stories are written by Latin American and Spanish authors, and they contain comprehension exercises aimed at improving students' Reading skills.

▶ *Guillermina Raffo Magnasco*   St. Thomas University

CUENTOS COMPLETOS (1968-2002).

Author: José Agustín

A compilation of one of Mexico's most important contemporary authors.

▶ *Teresa Chapa*   University of North Carolina at Chapel Hill

CUENTOS COMPLETOS.

Author: Julio Cortázar

Using the English short story tradition as a point of departure, Julio Cortázar — along with Jorge Luis Borges — made the short story in Spanish a very serious matter, literarily speaking. The literary innovation begun by Cortázar in both traditional time and the linear recitation of a story are ruptured, started a revolution which has become widely accepted and used in literature in Spanish ever since. However, Cortázar's short narratives are not limited to a renovation of styles and forms; each one of them, sometimes catalyzed by the quotidian, presents a fascinating and cinematographic story.

▶ *Lluís Agustí*   Instituto Cervantes New York

CUENTOS COMPLETOS.

Author: Silvina Ocampo

The youngest of the Ocampo sisters was not only a poet but an excellent writer of short stories, as was her husband, Adolfo Bioy Casares. Her stories are tragic, somber, full of ghostly figures and told with a certain touch of sadism or a spirit of perversion. They are a must-read.

▶ *Lluís Agustí*   Instituto Cervantes New York

CUENTOS DE CULVER CITY.

Author: José Luis Borau

NEW

Esteemed film director, screenwriter, producer, actor, critic, and historian with a long list of cinematic credits to his name has made significant scholarly contributions such as Diccionario del cine español (Madrid: Allianza, 2008), Cine español: una crónica visual desde 1896 hasta nuestros días (Barcelona: Lunwerg Editores, 2008), and Cuentos de cine: grandes narradores celebran el primer siglo del cine (Madrid: Santillana, 1996). In recent years, his narrative fiction has begun to get more attention. Loosely based on autobiographical experiences in Los Angeles, California – or the city of broken dreams – Cuentos de Culver City is his latest collection of short stories.

▶ *Claude Potts*   University of California

CUENTOS DE TIERRA Y EUCALIPTOS.

Author: Walter Ventosilla

NEW

Through twelve tales, the book CUENTOS DE TIERRA Y EUCALIPTOS gives back in poetic prose surroundings, experiences and situations typical of the rural zones in Peru but that could also be the reflection of many other towns in America. In each short story you get a glimpse of the characters whose lives go from the common to the legendary, framed in a day-to-day life that blends with celebrations and popular traditions. The atmosphere, the natural environment also amuses like another one of the characters showing communion among the men and women of the Andean towns with nature, with its religiousness, myths and beliefs.

▶ *Nellie B. Mulkay*  N Y State Spanish Bilingual Education Technical Assistance Center at NYU

CUENTOS del GALLO de ORO.

Authors: Juan Pedro Aparicio, Luis Mateo Diez, José María Merino
NEW

This group of Spanish authors is known as Los Filandones. They have made it their mission to revive the oral tradition of the Northeast of Spain and wrote these stories for this purpose. Beautifully illustrated by Toño Benavides, this collection is great for reading aloud or curled up in a chair.

▶ *Teresa Mlawer* Lectorum Publications

LA DAMA del ALBA.

Author: Alejandro Casona
NEW

On the night of the fiesta of San Juan, Death, in the form of a beautiful pilgrim, appears in a village in rural Asturias. In an atmosphere that is both mysterious and magical, reflecting many of the popular beliefs of the time, death is portrayed as deeply human. She is so human that we begin to feel pity for her because we see that she has no choice about what she does and until the end of the play does not even know who it is she has come to take with her.

▶ *Richard Heyer* Biblioteca "Jorge Luis Borges"

DEL AMOR y OTROS DEMONIOS.

Author: Gabriel García Márquez
NEW

A story of mystical and spiritual discovery. Love and other demons is the story of a young girl who captures the heart of a Priest. Her story continues to live on even after death. A must read if you like mystical tales.

▶ *Marshall García* Dominican University, Chicago

EL DELIRIO de TURING.

Author: Edmundo Paz Soldán

Paz Soldán uses the world of computer hacking to explore the stuggle between oppressed and oppressor. As he works to crack the codes in what has become an information war, Miguel Sáenz, who has taken the nom de guerre of Turing, discovers that his allies are seriously compromised. Winner of Bolivia's Premio Nacional de Novela in 2002.

▶ *David Block* Cornell University

DELIRIO.

 Author: Laura Restrepo

Winner of the Premio Alfaguara de novela in 2004, the plot revolves around Aguilar, an unemployed professor, and his search for his missing wife. Set in Restrepo's native Colombia, the novel elicits the country's tropes of drug dealing and money laundering but also explores the daily lives of people struggling to survive.

▶ *David Block*   Cornell University

LOS DETECTIVES SALVAJES.

 Author: Roberto Bolaño

One of the few recent attempts to create the great and total novel in the Spanish language.

▶ *José María Conget*   Writer

DÍAS CONTADOS.

 Author: Juan Madrid   NEW

Juan Madrid, former news journalist, erupted onto the literary scene at the start of the 90s with this intense and highly urban work, in which an ambitious photographer charged with producing a guide about the movement, finds himself immersed in a world inhabited by characters who reflect the cruel end of the dream of an entire generation.

▶ *Paloma Graciani*   Biblioteca "José Emilio Pacheco"

DISTINGUIDA SEÑORA.

 Author: Carmen Imbert Brugal

This novel takes place in a transitional period from tyranny to democracy following the death of dictator Rafael Trujillo in the Dominican Republic. It is a time of historical confusion where there is breakdown of social and moral values, giving birth to feminist liberalism. It tells the story of a woman in search of life's pleasures within a spurious social legitimacy.

▶ *Sarah Aponte*   Dominican Studies Institute.CUNY

DON QUIJOTE DE LA MANCHA.

Author: Miguel de Cervantes

What can one say about everyone's idealistic hero and his faithful sidekick. Always popular and studied in Spanish and literature classes and in translation, this classic should be read and re-read at different stages of one's life.

▶ *Millie Torrance*   Sacramento Public Library

DOÑA BÁRBARA.

Author: Rómulo Gallegos
NEW

A classic of Latin American literature this novel tells the return of Santos Luzardo to a ranch in the Venezuelan plains and his meeting with Doña Bárbara. It is an analysis of the society of the Venezuela plains, and the country in general. It represents the conflict between civilization and barbarism.

▶ *Norma Medina Ortiz*   Seminole County Public Library System

DOS CRÍMENES.

Author: Jorge Ibargüengoitia
NEW

"The story I am about to tell begins on a night when the police violated the constitution." The narrator continues to describe how he fled Mexico City for a small town where he hopes to stay with his wealthy uncle and wait for the problem with the police to blow over. He arrives to find that his elderly uncle is very ill and his cousins are very suspicious of the motives for his visit. Many complications ensue.

▶ *Richard Heyer*   Biblioteca "Jorge Luis Borges"

EN BUSCA DE KLINGSOR.

Author: Jorge Volpi
NEW

Set in the aftermath of the Second World War, Americans and Germans alike become entangled in the hunt for Hitler's chief scientist, Klingsor. This lyrical detective novel encompasses nuclear physics, a love affair and the Nuremberg trials in a gripping introduction to the work of Mexico's Crack generation.

▶ *Alison Hicks*   University Colorado

42

EN EL ÚLTIMO AZUL.

Author: Carmen Riera

The Mallorcan writer Carmen Riera obtained the National Literature Prize granted annually by the Spanish Ministry of Culture for this novel, one of the best ever written about the crypto-Jews of Spain and about the last great Inquisitorial trials. Set in the 17th century, the novel is based on, sad to say, real events which took place in Palma de Mallorca. A group of xuetes (name by which the descendants of Mallorcan Jews were derisively known) prepares to flee toward Leghorn by sea, with its blue promise of liberty. A novel which depicts the religious intransigence of an era, but which also serves as a reflection on current attitudes. An excellent novel, beautifully written and recently translated into English.

▷ *Lluís Agustí*   Instituto Cervantes New York

ENSAYO DE UN CRIMEN.

NEW

Author: Rodolfo Usigli

Usigli, a poet, playwright, essayist and diplomat, experiments with the crime thriller by narrating the tribulations of a character who considers crime to be an art and a destiny. However, Usigli enriches the genre by his use of a series of characters and settings around the Mexican capital, thereby achieving an ironic examination of postrevolutionary Mexican society.

▷ *Paloma Graciani*   Biblioteca "José Emilio Pacheco"

EL ENTENADO.

Author: Juan José Saer

A journey to the beginnings of civilization and also a reflection on "otherness", on another language and way of life. A man who lived among Indians for ten years, and now as an old man, recounts his life.

▷ *Martha Berman*   Professor of Language and Literature

EL ENTIERRO DE CORTIJO.

Author: Edgardo Rodríguez Juliá

NEW

Edgardo Rodríguez Juliá, one of the most important writers in Puerto Rico, wrote this novel in 1983 and it is considered one of the seminal works of modern Puerto Rican literature. El entierro de Cortijo uses the death of Rafael Cortijo, one of the most famous musicians in the island to describe the roots of Afro Puerto Rican music and its impact in its society. As the processional travels through the working class and impoverish neighborhood streets alike, Rodríguez Juliá exposed the richness and contradictions of Puerto Rican society, black and white and all the colors in between, and immerses the reader in the richness of the music, and of the people who creat it and enjoy it.

▶ *Marisol Ramos*　　　　　　　　　　　　　　Universidad de Connecticut

ESCUELA DE MANDARINES.

Author: Miguel Espinosa

A classic of the Spanish Baroque written in the middle of the 20th century. A forgotten genius from Murcia, who in my judgment wrote the most important work of Spanish literature since Don Quixote.

▶ *Juan Carlos Vidal*　　　　　　　　　　　　Instituto Cervantes Chicago

EL ESTADIO DE MÁRMOL.

Author: Juan Bonilla

The best, to my mind, collection of stories by a young Spanish author.

▶ *José María Conget*　　　　　　　　　　　　　　　　　　Writer

EVA LUNA.

Author: Isabel Allende

When a text like Eva Luna's adventures can carry you out of the shadows of a snowy, wintery week North of Chicago, it has a place in everyone's shelf.

▶ *Adan Griego*　　　　　　　　　　　　Stanford University Libraries

FÁBULAS de una ABUELA EXTRATERRESTRE.

 Author: Daína Chaviano

NEW

This award winning classic of Latin American Science Fiction inter-twines three different stories occurring in different planets and planes of reality. The first story is the tale of the Zhife, fantastic winged beings with three eyes and psychic powers; they inhabit a technically primitive planet called Faidir. The second story is that of a young astronaut, Arlene, who is stranded on a planet called Rybel, and the third is about a young girl, Ana, who believes in the paranormal and lives in Havana. On some level, they are all aware of each other, and, together, yet separately, they contribute to unlocking the secret of the ancient talismans [the stone and the mirror] that will have far-reaching and potentially catastrophic consequences. Part Science fiction and part fairy tale, even Soio [Merlin from King Arthur's Court] and the Druids are characters in this dazzling sci-fi fable.

▶ *Radamés Suárez*   Queens Library

LA FAMILIA de PASCUAL DUARTE.

 Author: Camilo José Cela

This was the first novel of Nobel laureate Camilo José Cela and most translated of his long career. Naturalist in style, it relates with no holds barred the ruthless life of a murderer, a peasant from Extremadura by the name of Pascual Duarte. Although there is a constant state of alarm throughout the work and a savage tone which causes one to shudder, there is a certain lyricism in Duarte's personality, in spite of the brutality of his actions, he seems more of a victim of circumstances than their catalyst. The sensation which the novel caused outside of Spain seems to suggest that Pascual Duarte may be the confirmation of the Spanish topoi of violence and bloodthirstiness.

▶ *Claude Potts*   University of California

FARABEUF.

 Author: Salvador Elizondo

An avant-garde novel in which narrative time and the broadest perspectivism possible are completely suspended. It forms part of that opening toward the East embraced by other Mexican authors such as Octavio Paz and Sergio Pitol. A unique gem of the literary avant-garde in the world of Hispanic letters.

▶ *Juan Carlos Vidal*   Instituto Cervantes Chicago

FICCIONES.

 Author: Jorge Luis Borges

In this essential compilation of some of Borges' best short stories such as, Tlö, Uqbar, Orbis Tertius, La biblioteca de Babel and La lotería en Babilonia, the reader will encounter several of the themes that appear in many of Borges' works such as treachery, mirrors, loneliness, folk heroes, out of this world and the universe.

► *Alvaro Sanabria*   San Francisco Public Library

LA FIESTA DEL CHIVO.

 Author: Mario Vargas Llosa

Peruvian novelist and essayist, Mario Vargas Llosa, is one of Latin-American leading writers. In The Feast of the Goat, he recreates the final days of Dominican Republic dictator General Rafael Trujillo's evil regime.

► *Libbhy Romero*   Brooklyn Public Library

LA FORJA DE UN REBELDE.

 Author: Arturo Barea

A fundamental work to understand 20th century Spain. It consists of three autobiographical novels which cover his childhood and adolescence in Madrid, his military service in Morocco, and conclude with the Civil War years, illuminating the entire era.

► *Richard Heyer*   Instituto Cervantes New York

FORTUNATA Y JACINTA: DOS HISTORIAS DE CASADAS.

 Author: Benito Pérez Galdós

A classic 19th century novel set in Madrid, this is a thoroughly enjoyable tale full of politics and social customs of the period.

► *Lynn Shirey*   Harvard College Library

GALÍNDEZ.

 Author: Manuel Vázquez Montalbán

Exiled in the Dominican Republic after the Spanish Civil war, the Basque nationalist politician Jesús de Galíndez collaborated with the Dominican government. Later he moved to New York as representative of the Basque government in exile and perhaps as a CIA informant. At Columbia University he starts to work on a book about the inner workings of the Trujillo dictatorship. The secret police of the Dominican dictator kidnapped Galíndez in Manhattan in 1956 and transferred him to the island, where he was tortured and killed. An American woman investigates his disappearance in the 1980's.

▶ *Lluís Agustí*   Instituto Cervantes New York

GÁLVEZ Y EL CAMBIO DEL CAMBIO.

Author: Jorge Martínez Reverte
NEW

Third of a series featuring the ironic jornalist and accidental detective Julio Gálvez who began his literary adventures at the end of the 1970s. The ironic, entertaining and paradoxical dialogues recall the American thriller, as well as the anthropological pessimism which informs that genre, but endowed here with a cutting-edge sense of humor.

▶ *Paloma Graciani*   Biblioteca "José Emilio Pacheco"

LOS GIRASOLES CIEGOS.

 Author: Alberto Méndez

Four exceptional stories, posthumously published, by a 60 year old first-time author, who would never know the far-reaching effects of the quality of his work.

▶ *José María Conget*   Writer

LA GUARACHA DEL MACHO CAMACHO.

 Author: Luis Rafael Sánchez

With this work, Sánchez revolutionizes the Puerto Rican novel, bringing to light the musical and vertiginous rhythm of his people.

▶ *Sabrina Abreu*   Instituto Cervantes New York

GUZMÁN DE ALFARACHE.

Author: Mateo Alemán

A masterpiece of the picaresque genre, this novel is remarkable not only for its vivid narration of adventures and its philosophical observations, but also for its evocation of the life, morals and manners of the period of the Counter Reformation in Spain and Italy.

► *Eduardo de Lamadrid*   Trans-Lingual Communications Inc.

EL HABLADOR.

Author: Mario Vargas Llosa

An intriguing fable about an indigenous people in Peru's Amazon, and the white storyteller who crosses cultural boundaries.

► *Lynn Shirey*   Harvard College Library

HASTA EL FIN DE LOS CUENTOS.

Author: José María Conget

One of the principal characteristics of José María Conget's work, author for a happy few, is its humanity, especially in some of its more interesting manifestations, humor and curiosity. Coupled to this trait is an extensive knowledge of literature (both good and bad) and film. Hasta el fin de los cuentos is a magnificent compendium of tales about and for literature, a profound and beautiful book which is read with the ease of someone joined in hand to another who knows the way perfectly.

► *Lluís Agustí*   Instituto Cervantes New York

HASTA NO VERTE, JESÚS MÍO.

Author: Elena Poniatowska

Journalist and author Poniatowska based this testimonial novel on a series of interviews conducted with an indigenous woman who recounted her difficult struggle to survive in modern-day Mexico.

► *Teresa Chapa*   University of North Carolina at Chapel Hill

HECHOS, DICHOS, OCCURRENCIAS y ANDANZAS de BARDÍN el SUPERREALISTA.
Author: Max

NEW

One of Spain's chief graphic artists and novelists, Max (Francesc Capdevila), has written and drawn a set of surreal – or as he would have it, superreal narratives. The hero, Bardín finds himself in a number of situations that test his mettle or call into question the workings of the world. The stories explore philosophical ideas and the human mind with dark humor and elegant artwork.

▶ *Sarah G. Wenzel*   University of Chicago

HELENA o el MAR del VERANO.

Author: Julián Ayesta

Julian Ayesta's brief, lyrical, and exquisite evocation of memories of summer vacations during childhood. While Ayesta was not a prolific nor a successful author, this is without a doubt one of the most beautiful novels of childhood in Spanish literature of the 20th century.

▶ *Lluís Agustí*   Instituto Cervantes New York

HERENCIA: The Anthology of HISPANIC LITERATURE OF THE UNITED STATES.
Author: Nicolas Kanellos, ed.

Excellent Spanish/English collection of U.S. Hispanic stories!

▶ *Christine Peterson*   Marantha Academy

HERMANA MUERTE.

Author: Justo Navarro

Perhaps the best crafted novel by one of the best Spanish writers of recent generations, capable of creating a disturbing hard-boiled world seen through a lyrical gaze, in a refined language where the characters express the innermost basis of their actions.

▶ *Ernesto Pérez Zúñiga*   Instituto Cervantes

HERRUMBROSAS LANZAS.

Author: Juan Benet

This pentad represents Juan Benet's best work and, in my opinion, the best work ever written about the Spanish Civil War. A perfect symbiosis of a frame of reference and a decadent atmosphere from which emerges all the complexity of the human psyche.

▶ *Juan Carlos Vidal*   Instituto Cervantes Chicago

LA HIGUERA.

Author: Ramiro Pinilla

Many of us who have been devoted followers since we discovered the existence of literature back in the 60's -when we used to pass from hand to hand books edited by Pinilla in Libropueblo editions- are stunned by the phenomenon of Pinilla. In later years he has not only rewritten his monumental Green Valleys, Red Hills (Verdes valles, colinas rojas, 3 vol. Tusquets, 2005-2006), the first volume of which was first published in the 80's and which now culminates in this excellent trilogy, but also now offers us a surprising work called The Fig Tree (La Higuera), Set in his native Getxo, Pinilla creates a narrative centered on the thorny theme of political reprisals in the aftermath of the Civil War. The relation between the protagonist, a Falangist and author of the reprisals, and a boy, child of the victims, serves as the framework in which to brilliantly expose the irrationality of those years, which today we wish were prehistoric. We are fortunate to have this new offering by Ramiro Pinilla, a writer who is currently enjoying overdue recognition, after having received the Euskadi Prize for the Novel in 2005, the Critic's Award in 2005 and the National Narrative Award in 2006.

▶ *Miguel Valladares*   Dartmouth College

HIJO DE LADRÓN.

Author: Manuel Rojas

The adventures of Aniceto Hevia, the son of a thief ("hijo de ladrón") and protagonist of this novel is clearly a major achievement in mid-20th-century Chilean social literature. Writer Manuel Rojas did not need to probe his imagination or creativity to create his novels and short stories: an attentive ear for reproducing popular speech and a concern for putting day-to-day experiences down on paper was enough. Yet this novel surpasses all that, ensuring that Hijo de ladrón, its protagonist and Rojas's fiction overall become more than mere genre work, and transforming the most simple and local material into beautiful literature.

▶ *Lluís Agustí*   Instituto Cervantes New York

HIJOS SIN HIJOS.

 Author: Enrique Vila Matas

Audacious, unique and heterodox novel which could be interpreted as a "Brief History of Spain" in the second half of the 20th century. The protagonists of the various episodes are all sons without sons; persons who do not wish to have descendants, beings whose own nature distances them from society and who do not need help of any kind.

▶   *Paloma Celis Carbajal*   UW-Madison

HIPOTERMIA.

 Author: Alvaro Enrigue

Hypothermia is a fragmentary novel comprised of seemingly unconnected stories, but whose common denominator is the shocking and strange way which the narrator shifts his gaze over environments and situations which are equally fractured and inapprehensible. In part a product of his stay in the capital city of the United States, this effective exercise dissects the characters and antiheroes of everyday life, thereby allowing Alvaro Enrigue (1969) to deploy the narrative tools and instruments of the efficient and impassive scrutinizer of existences and ruins.

▶   *Bruno Hernández Piché*   Mexican Writer and Diplomat

HISTORIA DE UN ABRIGO.

 Author: Soledad Puértolas

A novel where numerous stories get intersected when the main character starts to look for her mother's coat. A look at the complexity of family relations.

▶   *Patricia Figueroa*   Brown University Library

HISTORIA DE UNA GAVIOTA Y DEL GATO QUE LE ENSEÑÓ A VOLAR.

 Author: Luis Sepúlveda

Nothing is more charming than this story for kids aged 8 to 88. Our big, fat, sweet cat finds a gull on the roof of a house when the owner is on vacation. The gull asks the cat to care for her egg until it hatches and to teach the hatchling how to fly, since she is about to die from the effects of an oil slick. Guess who helps the cat with this mission. A beautiful and poetic story.

▶   *Martha Berman*   Professor of Language and Literature

LA HISTORIA del REY TRANSPARENTE.

Author: Rosa Montero
NEW

This is an excellent book. Its subject is the physical, emotional, and spiritual journey of a woman during the medieval era. The book is simultaneously funny, tender, and inspiring. The ending leaves the reader yearning for a better world.

▶ *Rita Aurora Puig*   Arapahoe Library District

HISTORIAS de FAMAS y CRONOPIOS.

Author: Julio Cortázar

This is one of the most emblematic story collections of the 20th century. The stories alternate between the absurd and the tender, making this collection stand out for its originality without precedent.

▶ *Octavio Núñez*   US Librarian

HISTORIAS de HADAS para ADULTOS.

Author: Daína Chaviano
NEW

This collection of three novellas in one volume is a stylistic tour de force, written in most polished and refined language. A combination of fantasy and science fiction, it revisits numerous world myths and legends: the Arthurian cycle, Adam and Eve, the Flood, among others. The three novellas include many literary genres, from fantasy to horror, and contain literary flights which are rarely found in those popular genres.

▶ *Robert Zaman*   US Librarian

EL HOMBRE, la HEMBRA y el HAMBRE.

Author: Daína Chaviano
NEW

Winner of the Azorín Prize for the Novel in 1998, this work (included in university syllabi in both the U.S.A. and Europe) is perhaps the most representative novel of Cuban literature at the end of the century. A reflection of an entire generation, it is indispensable for understanding the social psychology and the spiritual dilemmas of the Cuban people. Its surprising prose and its fusing of fantasy and reality make memorable reading.

▶ *Octavio Núñez*   US Librarian

IMÁN.

Author: Ramón J. Sender

Imán was the first novel by the prolific Spanish writer Ramón J. Sender, exiled in the United States. A fictional retelling of his own experiences as a military physician during the Moroccan War, Spain's colonial war against the tribes of the Rif in the 1920's, the novel addresses the military incompetence and corruption of the Spanish army in Africa, and the atrocities of the campaign are related in a critical and realist style.

▶   *Lluís Agustí*   Instituto Cervantes New York

INCIERTA GLORIA.

Author: Joan Sales

Taken from a line of William Shakespeare, "The uncertain glory of an April day", the title of this novel, to my taste one of the best, and concomitantly perhaps one of the least known about Civil War, alludes to the proclamation of the Second Spanish Republic in April 1931. Constantly rewritten by its author, it was first published in a censored version in Spain, and then was published whole in French and in exile. Three characters and a War, that functions not as a setting but rather as a protagonist, with its interminable times of suspense at an inactive front, in lower Aragon, make room somehow for love and reflection. It includes descriptions of the struggles between communists and anarchists, the bombings of cities and the rebellions of the rearguard, the dispersion of 1939 and the sad and desolate aftermath.

▶   *Lluís Agustí*   Instituto Cervantes New York

EL INDIO.

Author: Gregorio López y Fuentes

Story of a nameless tribe of Indians living in the mountains of Mexico. A timeless tale of the manners and customs that have all but disappeared.

▶   *Angélica Hurtado Gracia*   Los Angeles Public Library

INDIOS EN REBELIÓN.

Author: Néstor Taboada Terán

The short-story collection Indios en rebelión is one of Bolivian writer Néstor Taboada Terán's best-known works. The narrative core of these stories — presented in a style that seems to branch in many directions — revolves around political and social events in mid-20th-century Bolivia.

▶   *Lluís Agustí*   Instituto Cervantes New York

INDUSTRIAS Y ANDANZAS DE ALFANHUÍ.

Author: Rafael Sánchez Ferlosio

Expelled from school, a child named Alfanhuí travels throughout Castile and comes to understand reality in an extraordinary and fantastic manner. Sánchez Ferlosio's clean, poetic and inimitable style in this novel will impress and surprise readers from the first sentence on, and will not abandon nor tire them. A small literary gem upon which time has been unable to make inroads.

▶ *Lluís Agustí*　　　　　　　　　Instituto Cervantes New York

INÉS DEL ALMA MÍA.

Author: Isabel Allende

NEW

In this novel, the renowned author relates the life of Inés Suárez, the first Spanish woman to reach Chile, and her relationship to the conquistador Pedro de Valdivia. One of the best works by this writer, celebrated in all corners of the globe.

▶ *Octavio Núñez*　　　　　　　　　　　US Librarian

LAS INQUIETUDES DE SHANTI ANDÍA.

Author: Pío Baroja

The action novel The restlessness of Shanti Andía forms part of Pío Baroja's trilogy The Sea (El mar), and has been a staple in the reading lists of many generations of Spanish youth and adolescents. It relates the adventures of Juan de Aguirre, a Basque sailor, and the uncle of Shanti Andia and the pirate Zaldumbide.

▶ *Lluís Agustí*　　　　　　　　　Instituto Cervantes New York

LA INVENCIÓN DE MOREL.

Author: Adolfo Bioy Casares

A fugitive narrates the imaginary and incredible story of tourists who arrive at the island where he is hiding out. The triangle formed by the scientist Morel, Faustine and the fugitive himself functions as a way of speculating on love and immortality. La invención de Morel is a fantastical, extraordinary work, perhaps Bioy Casares's best. With a prologue by his friend and partner in literary adventure, Jorge Luis Borges.

▶ *Lluís Agustí*　　　　　　　　　Instituto Cervantes New York

LA ISLA BAJO el MAR.

Author: Isabel Allende

NEW

This epic of racism and rebellion begins in Haiti and ends in New Orleans after the Haitian Revolution. The multi-faceted plot explores a complicated and troubled relationship between a slave owner and a slave whose ingenuity and resilience offset the novel's violence and injustice.

▶ *Nancy Klasterka*   Hoover Public Library

LA ISLA de los AMORES INFINITOS.

Author: Daína Chaviano

NEW

This novel could be classified a historical fantasy family saga set in a period that covers more than a century. Winner of the Gold Medal at the Florida Book Awards, it has been nominated for Ireland's IMPAC Dublin International Prize, probably the most important award in the English-speaking world given to a fictional work, with a value of 100,000 Euros. The novel has been translated into 25 languages.

▶ *Robert Zaman*   US Librarian

EL JUEGO del ÁNGEL.

Author: Carlos Ruiz Zafón

NEW

This book keeps the reader in intense suspense from beginning to end. It is the prequel to La sombra del viento. The reader enters the streets of an ancient and extremely mysterious Spain. It provides an intellectual mystery in which a writer sells his eternal soul in exchange for fame in this world.

▶ *Rita Aurora Puig*   Arapahoe Library District

EL JUGUETE RABIOSO.

Author: Roberto Arlt

A hybrid of the picaresque and existential novel, and taking violence, anguish and the impossibility of progress or redemption as thematic elements, Arlt's novel relates the formative years of Silvio Astier, which are marked by misery and by a series of constant errors and failures, that in the aggregate, constitute his life.

▶ *Lluís Agustí*   Instituto Cervantes New York

JUVENTUD EN ÉXTASIS.

Author: Carlos Cuauhtemoc Sánchez

A highly acclaimed author who provides his audience with fictional situations about problems teenagers will encounter in real life, and how to deal with them. The resolutions are not heavy handed and are meant for both teenagers and parents to learn how to deal with sexuality.

▶ *Angela Encinas*   San Bernardino Public Library

LA AMIGDALITIS DE TARZÁN.

Author: Alfredo Bryce Echenique

Internationally acclaimed Peruvian writer Alfredo Bryce Echenique portrays in his novel Tarzan's tonsillitis, a love story between Juan Manuel Carpio, a composer and singer from Peru, and Fernanda María de la Trinidad del Monte, a Salvadoran married to a Chilean exile. Although their love affair is mostly experienced through their letters, the reader follows their thirty-year relationship through their multiple escapades set in Paris, El Salvador, Chile, California, and London.

▶ *Libbhy Romero*   Brooklyn Public Library

LA MUJER DEL MAESTRO.

Author: Guillermo Martínez

Picks up the literature of relationships and feelings where Benedetti [The Respite (La tregua), the interesting Benedetti] and Onetti [The Goodbyes (Los adioses), As Sad as Her (Tan triste como ella), etc] left off, although never sufficiently explored due to the hyper-politicized of our literature. This short novel is written in a simple and elegant Spanish which recalls the masters of the Generation of 1898.

▶ *Mónica Flores Correa*   Professor and Writer

LA PIEL FRÍA.

Author: Albert Sánchez Piñol

In the best literary tradition of the adventure and gothic genres, (Conrad, Lovecraft, Poe), the novel Cold Skin recounts the adventures of a solitary lighthouse keeper in the southernmost region of the globe. On an island isolated from all civilization and battered by wind and cold, survival becomes paramount amid unknown creatures in one of the least traveled seas of the planet. An excellent work of fiction.

▶ *Lluís Agustí*   Instituto Cervantes New York

LA ÚLTIMA ESCALA del TRAMP STEAMER.

 Author: Alvaro Mutis

The voyages of the Alción, a dilapidated freighter, in search of occasional cargoes parallels, in imagery and sense, the shipwreck of the love of its Captain, the Basque Jon Iturri, for the Lebanese girl Warda Bashur, younger sister of the ship's owner. The search for one more port before the tramp steamer gives out corresponds to Jon's obstinate desire for Warda, to a love condemned to disaster beforehand, to a pair of lovers separated by an unbridgeable gulf.

▶　*Lluís Agustí*　　　　　　　　　　Instituto Cervantes New York

EL LABERINTO de la SOLEDAD.

Author: Octavio Paz

A work that explores the psyche of the Mexican people in relation to the United States.

▶　*Angela Encinas*　　　　　　　　San Bernardino Public Library

EL LÁPIZ del CARPINTERO.

Author: Manuel Rivas

Among authors writing in Galician, Manuel Rivas is one of the most well-known outside his native Galicia. The Carpenter's Pencil recounts the relationship between a prison guard, Herbal, and a physician, Daniel Da Barca, during the Civil War in Galicia. Dr. Da Barca is imprisoned because of his ideas and has fallen in love with Marisa Mallo, a daughter of the regime. Herbal is jealous of the doctor and avails himself of the pencil of a carpenter who had been shot in the temple. A magnificent literary work with an element of the magical.

▶　*Lluís Agustí*　　　　　　　　　　Instituto Cervantes New York

EL LAZARILLO de TORMES.

 Author: Anonymous

This is one of the classics of Spanish literature. Its searing social commentary may sometimes prove frightening to the reader, but at the same time it reflects the atmosphere of the age with more than a modicum of realism. Moreover, Lazarillo himself is such a strong and unforgettable character that he has become the archetypal anti-hero.

▶　*Mark Pendleton*　　　　　　　　Branigan Library Las Cruces NM

EL LECTOR NOVOHISPANO.

Author: José Joaquín Blanco, ed.

The Mexican novelist and essayist José Joaquín Blanco (Mexico City, 1951) has compiled in this volume the central poetical, narrative, theatrical and historical texts of the viceroyalty of New Spain, thereby rescuing an epoch of literary and cultural vigor and artistry which has been unjustly forgotten, and which becomes essential for a full understanding of today's Mexico. In the introductory essay, Blanco offers the reader an overview of the literary output of New Spain and its major figures, giving them the due truly owed to them because of their historical and literary value.

| Gaspar Orozco | Mexican Poet and Diplomat |

LIBRO DEL CABALLERO ZIFAR.

Author: Ferrand Martínez

The oldest Spanish romance of chivalry, written between 1299 and 1305. The work is a medley containing adaptations of saints lives, popular tales, adventures of knight errantry, miraculous ocurrences. The knight errantry of Zifar and his sons, and the episode of the Lady in the Lake are conceived in the spirit of Arthurian legends. El Ribaldo, squire to one of Zifar's sons, is a kind of forerunner to Sancho Panza, and introduces a refreshing note of picaresque realism and self-mockery.

| Eduardo de Lamadrid | Trans-Lingual Communications Inc. |

EL LIBRO DEL CONDE LUCANOR.

Author: Juan Manuel Infante de Castilla

El Conde Lucanor is Don Juan Manuel's great 14th century masterpiece, a collection of 50 moral tales or "exempla" in the style of Boccacio's Decameron, but anticipating it by more than a decade. The frame is provided by Count Lucanor's problems and his counselor Patronio's solutions, each in the form of a tale ending with a rhymed moral. The tales are composed in a lucid, informal and spirited style that set the standard for the age, and is relevant to our own.

| Eduardo de Lamadrid | Trans-Lingual Communications Inc. |

LOS LIBROS ARDEN MAL.

Author: Manuel Rivas

Narrative about the persecution of people and ideas in La Coruña during the Franco era, it recounts the burning of the books of the private library of Casares Quiroga, making reference to the minister, his wife and above all, his daughter, already a celebrated actress with the National Theater of Paris. In my opinion, this is a very good book because it skillfully combines history and fiction, leaving the reader with a bitter taste and a sense of the great injustice of Francoism, against ideas and persons, killing many and persecuting others.

▶ *Carmen de Zulueta*   Writer and Professor

LA LLUVIA AMARILLA.

Author: Julio Llamazares

La lluvia amarilla is the story of the death of a town in the province of Huesca in the Pyrenees as told by the last of its inhabitants, Andrés de Casa Sosas, a sick and lonely old man who during the last day of his life sees, in a kind of hallucination, some of the characters of the village which has witnessed his birth and now his death.

▶ *Lluís Agustí*   Instituto Cervantes New York

LO FUGITIVO PERMANECE.
20 CUENTOS MEXICANOS.

Author: Carlos Monsiváis, ed.

Selection of stories by nineteen Mexican writers published between 1934-1984. This anthology provides a representative sample of achievements and tendencies, of characters and customs from an era which witnessed the transformation of traditional Mexico into modern Mexico. The writers included in this anthology are: Juan de la Cabada, José Revueltas, Edmundo Valadés, Juan José Arreola, Elena Garro, Augusto Monterroso, Ricardo Garibay, Jorge Ibargüengoitia, Carlos Fuentes, Juan García Ponce, Juan Vicente Melo, Sergio Pitol, Elena Poniatowska, Eraclio Zepeda, José Emilio Pachecho, José Agustín, Héctor Aguilar Camín, Guillermo Samperio, Juan Villoro

▶ *Paloma Celis Carbajal*   UW-Madison

LO QUE ESTÁ EN MI CORAZÓN.

Author: Marcela Serrano

This is both, a self discovery novel and a political one set in Chiapas Mexico. I found it well written with wonderful descriptions of San Cristobal and an intriguing look at "zapatism".

▶ *Millie Torrance*   Sacramento Public Library

LOS DE ABAJO.

 Author: Mariano Azuela

Azuela's novel was one of the first to tackle the Mexican Revolution, and we can also say, one of the best and most truthful contemporary accounts, a magnificent portrait of a people and an era. The narrative of the military campaign and the personal experience of Demetrio Macías serves as a paradigm of the Mexican who lives, suffers, and fights in the Revolution, sometimes without a clear notion of motives, but impelled by forces beyond his control.

► *Lluís Agustí*   Instituto Cervantes New York

LUIS BANDOLERO LUIS.

Author: Walter Ventosilla   **NEW**

Brigandage focused its center of action in the Andean area of Perú up until mid-twentieth century. The most remembered is Luis Pardo. His criminal life was directed towards the bad authorities and the abuse that ranchers committed against the poor of the region, which he protected and by whom he was loved and worshipped. Luis Pardo died tragically in 1909. The book does not pretend to be a biography nor a chronicle of his adventures. On the contrary, from historical dates, Luis Bandolero Luis inquires on the legendary personage that led his existence with a permanent rebelliousness with the only social proposition of riding his horse and making justice by his own hands.

► *Nellie B. Mulkay*   N Y State Spanish Bilingual Education Technical Assistance Center at NYU

MALA ONDA.

Author: Alberto Fuguet

A coming of age novel set in Chile as Pinochet's dictatorship is confronting growing opposition.

► *Teresa Chapa*   University of North Carolina at Chapel Hill

MALDITO AMOR.

Author: Rosario Ferré   **NEW**

The fortunes of the de la Valle family beginning on a sugar plantation and continuing into a San Juan rocked by violence are described in a novella followed by three related short stories. The stories of Don Julio, Doña Elvira and their descendants reflect the social changes in Puerto Rico during the Twentieth Century while raising many questions about race, religion and the possibilities of independence.

► *Richard Heyer*   Biblioteca "Jorge Luis Borges"

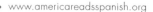

LA MANO DE FÁTIMA.

 Author: Ildefonso Falcones

NEW

Falcones paints a portrait of the tensions that existed in late 16th century Spain for those caught between love for their country and desire to openly practice the Muslim religion. Through Hernando, his main character, the author speaks of the hope for a more peaceful co-existence between the Christian West and the Muslim East.

▶ *Nancy Klasterka*    Hoover Public Library

LAS MANOS DEL PIANISTA.

 Author: Eugenio Fuentes

NEW

Considered by the critics to be one of the new innovators of the crime thriller in Europe. Eugenio Fuentes has published works in more than a dozen countries, notably those of the series whose protagonist is the detective Ricardo Cupido. This time Cupido delves into an enthralling investigation, where alibis do not matter as much as the cloudy and desolate descriptions of the human condition.

▶ *Paloma Graciani*   Biblioteca "José Emilio Pacheco"

MAÑANA EN LA BATALLA, PIENSA EN MI.

Author: Javier Marías

NEW

Fascinating incident told like a detective novel that allows reader to think about philosophy.

▶ *Mark Alvarez*    Salk Lake City Library

MARES DEL SUR.

Author: Noé Jitrik

NEW

On December 31st Inspector Malerba (an only slightly corrupt police officer) is called on to deal with what seems to be a minor family feud in a quiet neighborhood of Mar del Plata. His investigation of that fight leads him to an unsolved murder which had occurred a few months previous. He continues to search for answers even after it becomes clear that people at very high levels of the military government are involved in the crime. As a result the situation becomes very complicated.

▶ *Richard Heyer*   Biblioteca "Jorge Luis Borges"

MARGARITA, ESTÁ LINDA LA MAR.

Author: Sergio Ramírez   NEW

For this excellent work, this Nicaraguan writer won Alfaguara Prize for the Novel in 1998. In this novel, Rubén Darío, Anastasio Somoza, and a sizeable cross-section of Nicaraguan society make appearances during the period from 1907, year in which Rubén Darío returns to his native land, until Somoza is assassinated. Sergio Ramírez has fashioned here an apt metaphor of the political and cultural history of Nicaragua.

▶ *Salvador Vergara*   Instituto Cervantes Chicago

MÁSCARAS.

Author: Leonardo Padura   NEW

One of the few Cuban writers who, from Cuba, dares to offer a critical vision of the social situation, Padura continues with Máscaras the tretalogy Cuatro estaciones, whose protagonist is police Lieutenant Mario Conde. By means of the adventures of this character and his cases, the author sketches a portrait of the small virtues and great miseries of present-day Cuba.

▶ *Paloma Graciani*   Biblioteca "José Emilio Pacheco"

MATERIA PRIMA: PROTONOVELA.

Author: Marcio Veloz Maggiolo

The story is told through the life of Ariel, who upon returning to Santo Domingo, finds himself with the task of complying with the dying wish of his friend Persio. Persio turns over letters, interviews, notes and drafts of chapters to Ariel and charges him with writing and publishing the novel which the former wasn't able nor will be able to create. This "Raw Material" will make Ariel confront the past, from which the not very pleasant experiences of the neighborhood's inhabitants during the years of the Trujillo will resurface. A kind of magic envelops the characters and the city and creates a complex story.

▶ *Sarah Aponte*   Dominican Studies Institute. CUNY

LOS MEJORES CUENTOS.

Author: Sergio Pitol   NEW

Winner of the Cervantes Prize in 2005, Pitol is one of Mexico's most compelling and imaginative contemporary writers. This book is comprised of 14 stories ordered chronologically but with very different geographical settings, each of which is related in some very special way to Mexico. As the writer himself asserts, these 14 stories form a kind of literary autobiography.

▶ *Salvador Vergara*   Instituto Cervantes Chicago

MELODRAMA.

Author: Jorge Franco

Vidal, a handsome young man, one day discovers a mark on his neck that is the warning of a fatal illness. Since he's not able to tell Perla the disgrace, he abandons her. He prefers that she make false suppositions. It seems that Vidal dies soon and his condition as an omniscient dead man allows him to tell us about his life and family. But Vidal isn't dead and his relationship with Perla isn't what we believe it to be at the beginning. The unravelling of the intrigue happens in small doses that keeps us on edge for nearly 400 pages.

▶   *Tom LaSalle*   Ferguson Library

MEMORIAS DE ALTAGRACIA.

Author: Salvador Garmendia

Salvador Garmendia is one of the most interesting novelists to come out of Venezuela in the 20th century. As García Márquez does with Macondo, Garmendia makes Memorias de Altagracia into a marvelous nostalgic journey through childhood and the rural world that disappears in adulthood, which he tries to preserve in this work.

▶   *Lluís Agustí*   Instituto Cervantes New York

MEMORIAS DE MAMA BLANCA.

Author: Teresa de la Parra
                                                                NEW

The narrator introduces the book as the "suaves recuerdos" (gentle memories) of Mama Blanca. On the surface full of nostalgia, the political and social conflict of 19th century Venezuela are always in the background. Humble workers on the hacienda are described with great tenderness, among them Vicente Cochocho who occasionally disappears to lead rebels whor are fighting against the government.

▶   *Richard Heyer*   Biblioteca "Jorge Luis Borges"

MÉXICO ANTE DIOS.

Author: Francisco Martín Moreno
                                                                NEW

A well-written and entertaining historical novel covering the large — and for the author, nefarious — part the Catholic Church played in 19th century Mexican history. One of a series of historical novels by this author. In their scope these remind me of Gore Vidal's historical novels and Martín Moreno's works similarly should be in every popular collection. Others in this series include "México Negro" and "México Acribillado."

▶   *Mark Rex*   Salt Lake City Public Library

MI VESTIDO VERDE ESMERALDA.

Author: Alister Ramírez Márquez

NEW

Mi vestido verde esmeralda tells the story of an extraordinary woman, Clara, living in the Colombian Andes during the 20th century. It is a story that not only portrays her suffering, the protagonist, but also reflects the long and arduous physical and methaphysical journey of immigrant women to unknown lands.

▶ *Nellie B. Mulkay*   N Y State Spanish Bilingual Education Technical Assistance Center at NYU

MILAGROS DE NUESTRA SEÑORA.

Author: Gonzalo de Berceo

Berceo is the earliest known poet in Spanish literature and the first representative of the "mester de clerecía" school. This great religious poem, presented as a collection of 25 tales, is written is an intimate, personal style. Berceo interspersed his narrative with simple humor and realistic homely detail which accentuate his at times almost mystical reverence. His populism and rustic language continue to exercise their spell and charm the modern reader. His other best known work is a vivid account of the life of Santo Domingo de Silos.

▶ *Eduardo de Lamadrid*   Trans-Lingual Communications Inc.

EL MISTERIO DE LA CRIPTA EMBRUJADA.

Author: Eduardo Mendoza

A very satiric, gothic novel set in Barcelona.

▶ *Lynn Shirey*   Harvard College Library

MISTERIOSA BUENOS AIRES.

Author: Manuel Mujica Lainez

By means of a series of chronologically arranged stories, the Argentine writer Mujica Lainez reconstructs the history of Buenos Aires since its foundation to the 20th century. An exquisite reconstruction of characters and epochs through the superb gifts for narrative and evocation by the author of another of the greatest novels in Spanish of all time, Bomarzo.

▶ *Lluís Agustí*   Instituto Cervantes New York

LA MUERTE DE ARTEMIO CRUZ.

 Author: Carlos Fuentes

Mexican novelist Fuentes narrates the events of Artemio Cruz's life on his death bed in various voices. One reviewer wrote that before dying Cruz examines the value of his existence.

▶ *Millie Torrance*   Sacramento Public Library

LA MUERTE Y LA DONCELLA.

 Author: Ariel Dorfman   NEW

Death and the Maiden, a theatrical work by this renowned Chilean writer, was originally published in 1991 and taken to the screen by Roman Polanski in 1994. Dorfman (poet, playwright, novelist, essayist, and fervent human rights activist) has also been Professor of Spanish Literature at the University of Chile, the University of Amsterdam, the Sorbonne (Paris IV), the University of California-Berkeley, and the University of Maryland. Since 1985 he has been a Professor of Latin American Studies at Duke University and a researcher at many other universities in the United States. In 1971, in collaboration with Armand Mattelert, he wrote Reading Donald Duck, where both describe the ideological components of the animations of Walt Disney, from the perspective of both Marxist and psychoanalytic theories. This work was the impetus for much subsequent research into the ideological impact of children's literature, including Babar the Elephant and the Lone Ranger, as well as into other manifestations of mass culture.

▶ *Marcelo Ayala*   Instituto Cervantes Chicago

MUERTOS DE PAPEL.

 Author: Alicia Giménez Bartlett   NEW

The popularity of Alicia Giménez Bartlett and her character, Inspector Petra Delicado, provides definite proof that the detective novel does not have to remain an exclusively male genre.

▶ *Paloma Graciani*   Biblioteca "José Emilio Pacheco"

MUJERES DE OJOS GRANDES.

 Author: Angeles Mastretta

Set in Puebla, Mexico the stories recount the traditions and lives of Mexican women in past decades.

▶ *Millie Torrance*   Sacramento Public Library

EL MUNDO.
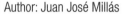

Author: Juan José Millás NEW

This book of memoirs in novel form, deals principally with childhood and touches upon adolescence. Millás offers us his own very particular vision of the events of his childhood in a luminous, expansive, and Mediterranean Valencia, contrasted with Madrid, rather with a street in Madrid, where everything is colder and grayer, although still full of surprises. Through Millás' gaze, his own family, the neighbors, friends, and the lost parade with humor and bitterness through that private universe that becomes his street. For those encountering the work of Juan José Millás for the first time, this work could be a good starting point for understanding the world, the characters, and the phobias which populate his novels and articles. It's as if the author has lain on the psychoanalyst's couch, and through the course of 233 pages, emptied (and that is one of the novel's strengths) the contents of his mind. This novel gained the author the Planeta Prize of 2007.

▶ *Salvador Vergara*   Instituto Cervantes Chicago

EL MUNDO ALUCINANTE.

Author: Reinaldo Arenas

This is the story of one amazing character, the candid and picaresque Fray Servando, a Latin American hero who finds himself fighting against the Spanish Inquisition during the time of the Mexican independence wars. The novel is a dialogue between fiction and history, fantasy and magic, where some events are told from several perspectives. A whimsical, amazing read.

▶ *Alina San Juan*   Trade Comission of Spain

EL MUNDO HA VIVIDO EQUIVOCADO.

Author: Roberto Fontanarrosa NEW

Humor book based on real life stories and popular culture.

▶ *Rafael Pérez Mercado*   Biblioteca Pública Raquel Quiñones

LOS MUNDOS QUE AMO.

Author: Daína Chaviano NEW

This book, despite being classified as literature for juveniles, can be perfectly enjoyed by adults as well. Although putatively a work of fiction, it is narrated in such a convincing manner that the reader begins to doubt if what he or she is reading is real or science fiction. I would classify it as a classic of Hispanic American contemporary science fiction for youngsters.

▶ *Robert Zaman*   US Librarian

LA NADA COTIDIANA.

Author: Zoe Valdés

This is a feminist novel about the life of a woman in Cuba during the Castro regime. It is a very modern novel.

> *Natalie Romano*   Colorado Supreme Court Law Library

NADA.

Author: Carmen Laforet

A feminist novel about a yound woman who moves to Barcelona to study in the wake of the Spanish Civil War.

> *Patricia Figueroa*   Brown University Library

NADIE ENCENDÍA LAS LÁMPARAS.

Author: Felisberto Hernández

This just may be my favorite collection of short stories ever. Writing long before the magical realism captivated the world's attention, Uruguayan composer, pianist and writer Felisberto Hernández was churning out fantastical and quintessentially surreal stories all by himself in Montevideo. Italo Calvino called him as "a writer like no other: like no European, nor any Latin American. He is an 'irregular' who eludes all classification and labeling, yet he is unmistakable on any page to which one might randomly open one of his books."

> *Claude Potts*   University of California

NARRACIONES.

Author: Jorge Luis Borges

These are short stories by Jorge Luis Borges. I recommend it because the author was well-known, and the stories are acknowledged all over the world.

> *Guillermina Raffo Magnasco*   St. Thomas University

NIEBLA.

Author: Miguel de Unamuno

A key work in Spanish literature. In this novel, Unamuno tackles once again the golden theme of the ambiguity between reality and fiction, and combines it with the narrative innovation of dialogues between the creator and his characters.

> *Paloma Celis Carbajal*   UW-Madison

NO PASÓ NADA.

Author: Antonio Skármeta
NEW

The story is about Lucho and his family having to abruptly leave Chile during the Pinochet dictatorship. The family immigrates to Germany upon learning that the father has been placed on "The List". Lucho, like so many other children of families who immigrate, has to quickly adapt to the German way to help his parents. Things are not easy for Lucho either. He has a bit of a rough time with the language, culture, and even the weather. Adapting takes time and problems arise during the acculturation process but Lucho ingeniously overcomes these and matures through the process.

▶ *Alma Ortega*   University of San Diego

NO SERÁ LA TIERRA.

Author: Jorge Volpi

This novel narrates the great transformations of our time: the fall of the Berlin Wall, the coup d'etat against Gorbachev, Yeltsin's ascension to power, germ warfare and the Human Genome Project. In a style both elegant and profound, Volpi explores the avarice, the passion and the egotism which move human beings, within the political-historical context of globalization.

▶ *Juan Pablo Debesis*   Lectorum

NOMBRE DE TORERO.

Author: Luis Sepúlveda
NEW

In this magisterial novel, Luis Sepúlveda presents a gallery of characters marked with the sign of failure. Insurance agents, German spies, and a series of rootless Chileans appear in a story that covers the history of world politics in the last decades of the 20th century. His background themes are the failure of utopias and the need to survive in spite of all obstacles and failures.

▶ *Paloma Graciani*   Biblioteca "José Emilio Pacheco"

LA NOVELA DE MI VIDA.

Author: Leonardo Padura
NEW

A Cuban professor of literature based in Spain returns to Cuba for the purpose of finding a lost manuscript of the 19th century poet José María Heredia and of finding out who was the childhood friend who traduced him as a counterrevolutionary and caused him to go into exile.

▶ *Rafael E. Tarrago*   University of Minnesota

NOVELAS EJEMPLARES.

Author: Miguel de Cervantes

The best short narratives in the Spanish language. Others probably named Don Quixote, the obvious selection. But this volume definitively changed the course of short fiction in the Spanish language and profoundly influenced other European literatures. No subsequent novelist has escaped its influence.

▷ *Isaías Lerner* CUNY

LA NOVIA DE ODESSA.

Author: Edgardo Cozarinsky

Relatively unknown until now by the public at large, Edgardo Cozarinsky is an Argentine filmmaker and writer who has resided in Paris since 1974. The Bride of Odessa (La novia de Odessa) is an excellent work from the literary point of view, combining fiction and memory in a fascinating way. The intertwined personal stories of Cozarinsky's Jewish oral memory leads us to reflect on the meaning and truthfulness of origins and history.

▷ *Lluís Agustí* Instituto Cervantes New York

LA NOVIA OSCURA.

Author: Laura Restrepo

This is one of the best of Latin American novels published in the last 20 years. This book has been praised as factual, beautiful, funny, perceptive, luminous and unforgettable.

▷ *Alvaro Sanabria* San Francisco Public Library

NUBOSIDAD VARIABLE.

Author: Carmen Martín Gaite

An intense and intimate contemporary novel about a mature woman's friendship and the nature of writing.

▷ *Lynn Shirey* Harvard College Library

OBABAKOAK.

Author: Bernardo Atxaga

Bernardo Axtaga is among those Basque writers whose work has been recognized and widely disseminated beyond the borders of Eusquera. His best-known is perhaps Obabakoak, which received the National Literature Prize granted by the Spanish Ministry of Culture. Obabakoak is a collection of finely honed, humorous and ironic short stories. The stories are all set in Obaba, a somewhat magical imaginary region in the Basque country. A magnificent work of universal scope.

▶ *Lluís Agustí*   Instituto Cervantes New York

OBRAS COMPLETAS (Y OTROS CUENTOS).

Author: Augusto Monterroso

"God has not yet created the world; he is only imagining it, as if he were half asleep. That is why the world is perfect, but confused," is both the beginning and end of one of Augusto Monterroso's stories. This author's works are always short; they are subtly ironic more than humorous. Better known as Tito, Monterroso—a native of Guatemala—is the reason this literary genre predicated on brevity has achieved maturity in Spanish. A clean and pleasant read, and highly recommended.

▶ *Lluís Agustí*   Instituto Cervantes New York

EL OBSCENO PÁJARO DE LA NOCHE.

Author: José Donoso

The voice which narrates this eminent work from the Latin American boom flows indefatigably from the lips of the Little Mute, as in a voyage from being to nothingness, creating a cavernous and decrepit world. A world which from the first to last page acquires the dimension of a universe from which the reader cannot escape.

▶ *Juan Pablo Debesis*   Lectorum

OCHENTA Y SEIS CUENTOS.

Author: Quim Monzo

NEW

Possessing an ironic, diverting, surrealistic, and tender style which is unmistakable, Quim Monzo is able to give his stories such unexpected turns which lead the reader to reflection, and for a time, confusion. Monzo is one of the essential short story authors, and has been translated widely into Spanish and English from his native Catalan.

▶ *Salvador Vergara*   Instituto Cervantes Chicago

OJO POR DIENTE.

Author: Rubén Bareiro Saguier

The Paraguayan poet and storyteller Rubén Bareiro offers in this work eleven stories of a social character about the reality as lived in Paraguay. Although this statement may appear superfluous, and perhaps also due to his experiences of persecution and exile, language, the word, assumes pride of place in this book, and in all of Bareiro's work. In his stories flows his poetry, a poetry expressed both in Spanish and Guaraní. The resulting multiplicity of sonorous registries allows the poet to delve deeply into language, into all languages, into the formal beauty of words and images. An author that needs to be rediscovered.

▶ *Lluís Agustí*   Instituto Cervantes New York

OLIMPITA.

Authors: Hernán Migoya y Joan M. Marín   **NEW**

Written by Migoya and drawn by Marín, this graphic novel tells the story of fishmonger Olimpita García García who falls in love with a Senegalese immigrant, upending her life. The neighborhood in which she and her husband, immigrants themselves from Andalucía to Catalonia, live is carefully portrayed. The difficulties of immigration, from broken dreams, uprootedness and loss of identity, to poverty and despair are starkly evident, in part through the destabilizing use of both Catalan and Spanish.

▶ *Sarah G. Wenzel*   University of Chicago

OPERACIÓN MASACRE.

Author: Rodolfo Walsh   **NEW**

A pioneering work in the genre of the non-fiction novel, which relates a real event in novelized form, namely, the execution by firing squad of groups of civilians suspected of having formed part of counter-coup against the military dictatorship in 1956. As such, Walsh introduces political criticism into the police story, and enriches the genre. Committed to the revolution to the very end, he joined the list of those sadly known as the disappeared of the Argentine dictatorship.

▶ *Paloma Graciani*   Biblioteca "José Emilio Pacheco"

EL OSCURECER.

Author: Luis Mateo Díez

The wise desolation of old age is depicted in this fable where the real and the symbolic appear magisterially fused in the cereal fields which surround an old train station. Composed as an intimate confidence made to the reader, this is one of the best works in Spanish of the modern era.

▶ *Ernesto Pérez Zúñiga*   Instituto Cervantes

OSCURO BOSQUE OSCURO.

Author: Jorge Volpi

NEW

In 1945 in Hitler's Germany, 500 civilians – bakers, tailors and old men no longer fit for combat - were trained to exterminate their Jewish neighbors. Volpi takes this incident out of its historical context and places it in a non-specific everywhere, a sad sequence of events that demonstrates the depths to which humans can sink and have sunk.

▶ *Sara Martínez*   Tulsa City-County Library

LA OTRA MANO DE LEPANTO.

Author: Carmen Boullosa

A reformulation in a contemporary key of Cervantes' Gitanilla from the Exemplary Novels and of the legendary Battle of Lepanto, in which the heroine is a combatant aboard the galleon La Real. María the Dancer observes the passage of the century in this intensely literary work, whose pages follow one another in such quick succession that the reader is literally left breathless. This monumental and fortunate novel confirms the Mexican writer as a major novelist of her generation in an international context.

▶ *Juan Pablo Debesis*   Lectorum

PANTALEÓN Y LAS VISITADORAS.

Author: Mario Vargas Llosa

The misfortunes of the honest Captain Pantaleón Pantoja, obliged to organize an army of women to help pacify Peruvian troops in the Amazon jungle, revolutionized the life of the region. A delectable and hilarious novel about efficiency, military devotion, and desire.

▶ *Lluís Agustí*   Instituto Cervantes New York

PARADISO.

Author: José Lezama Lima

Masterpiece of the great poet Lezama Lima, considered to be an immense poem in prose, almost unique in the whole of literature in Spanish. The special atmosphere of this book has been compared favorably with Marcel Proust's In search of lost time.

▶ *Fernando Velázquez Medina*　　　　　　　　　Writer and Journalist

PARAÍSO TRAVEL.

Author: Jorge Franco

Colombian author Jorge Franco depicts in his novel Paradise Travel the adventures of the undocumented. Marlon, who is in love with Reina, decides to leave his home in Medellin, Colombia by following her to New York instead of going to university.

▶ *Libbhy Romero*　　　　　　　　　　　　　　Brooklyn Public Library

LA PARRANDA.

Author: Eduardo Blanco Amor

A esmorga (Out on the Town in Spanish La Parranda), was the first narrative work in Galician published by Blanco-Amor and represents one of the most unique works in all of Galician literature. It is distinguished by the richness of the language, the sense of humor common to great part of the author's oeuvre, and a picaresque world heretofore unknown in Galician letters. The great Portuguese philosopher Rodríguez Lapa referred to it as a strange and powerful novel, whose characters appear, strong and palpable, in old Auria, speaking a language of excellent popular flavor. "It lacks nothing in order to be considered a small masterpiece."

▶ *Xosé Luis García Canido*　　　　　　　　　　Instituto Cervantes

LOS PASOS PERDIDOS.

Author: Alejo Carpentier

One of the most important novels of Latin American literature of all times, it synthesizes the styles and themes of this distinguished author, one of the most ingenious writers in Western literature. Received an award for best foreign novel published in France in 1956.

▶ *Fernando Velázquez Medina*　　　　　　　　　Writer and Journalist

LOS PECES DE LA AMARGURA.

Author: Fernando Aramburu

Fifth novel of this already consecrated Basque author born in San Sebastián in 1959, and the first written about a typically Basque subject. From Germany, where he resides teaching Spanish language and literature as a professor of the University of Lippstandt, Aramburu has "thrust" upon us a stark, multiple-voiced novel focused on the theme of ETA violence and its social repercussions. Using a fragmented narrative as a stylistic device to perhaps avoid sentimentality, Aramburu has produced an excellent indictment against all forms of fanaticism. Before closing this brief summary, I would like to emphasize that the literary merits of this excellent author are now being recognized not only by literary critics (refer to Fernando Aramburu, Storyteller, written by Jose Manuel Diaz de Guereñu) but also by European publishers, as witnessed by the recent translation of The Trumpeter of Utopia (El trompetista del Utopía) into Italian, added to the translation into German of his first novel Fires with lemon (Fuegos con Limón).

▶ *Miguel Valladares*   Dartmouth College

PEDRO PÁRAMO.

Author: Juan Rulfo

Pedro Páramo is one of the most important Mexican novels ever written. Besides its elaborate plot and complex characters, this text is notable for reflecting rural life in Mexico after the revolution.

▶ *Paloma Celis Carbajal*   UW-Madison

PEQUEÑAS RESISTENCIAS:
ANTOLOGÍA DEL NUEVO CUENTO ESPAÑOL.
Author: Andrés Neuman, ed.

This anthology of thirty young Spanish short story writers, born in the 1960's and 1970's, is a strong collection based on literary quality, innovation and which contains names both canonical and truly unknown. Included is a brief biographical sketch of each other. "A short story feast."

▶ *Lluís Agustí*   Instituto Cervantes New York

PERCUSIÓN.

Author: José Balza

A novel in which a character undertakes, with sensibility and intelligence, a voyage around the world, and becomes enlightened as to the abyss and splendors of human relations, sex, friendship, philosophy and history. Percusión advances like the exercising of a memory interwoven in a great game with temporality and with some of the social and individual milestones of contemporary history.

▶ *Ernesto Pérez Zúñiga*   Instituto Cervantes

PERSÉPOLIS.

Author: Marjane Satrapi
                                            NEW

This graphic novel recounts the 1979 Islamic Revolution in Iran, from the perspective of a 10-year-old school girl.

▶ *Martin Corrigan*   Houston Public Library

PLATA QUEMADA.

Author: Ricardo Piglia
                                          NEW

Piglia fictionalizes a real event that took place in Argentina in 1965. The event was a bank robbery with the covert participation of various police officers and politicians, the treachery of the bank robbers who decide to flee with the money and the subsequent police chase. In preparing the novel, the author had access to confidential materials (court witnesses, the transcription of the secret recordings made by the police during the robbery, the testimonial declarations, and journalistic accounts) that allow him to reconstruct the events and plot, the characters and their speech, and the time in general, with great precision.

▶ *Paloma Graciani*   Biblioteca "José Emilio Pacheco"

PLATERO Y YO.

Author: Juan Ramón Jiménez

This is an enchanting book, full of grace, tenderness and nostalgia for idyllic past. Moreover, Jiménez writes with such beauty and elegance that it almost breaks your heart.

▶ *Mark Pendleton*   Branigan Library Las Cruces NM

LA PLAZA del DIAMANTE.

Author: Mercè Rodoreda

The most celebrated novel in 20th century Catalan literature and the most representative of the author's work.

▶ *Jaume Martí Olivella*   University of New Hampshire

PLENILUNIO.

Author: Rogelio Sinán

Plenilunio is the title of what may be Panamanian author Rogelio Sinán's best-known novel, .written in the 1940s. Influenced by surrealist techniques, Sinán (a pseudonym adopted by Bernardo Domínguez Alba) set this interesting tale in a cabaret on the Panama Canal.

▶ *Lluís Agustí*   Instituto Cervantes New York

POR donde SALE el SOL.

Author: Blanca Valdecasas

NEW

A man becomes a widower (this is not stated, but one intuits it, since the wife appears at the beginning). They have the perfect marriage, they love and adore each other, they live in Madrid and have 7 children! He is a painter and at that time he finds himself short of ideas and imagination, so they decide to pick up sticks and move to other side of the world, to Chile. The things that happen to them once they arrive in Chile are both comical and sad, but the author describes it all with great affection for her characters and a great sense of humor. I was moved, especially by the descriptions of the Chilean landscape, the very peculiar characters who parade through its pages, and the interior world of the protagonist, who tries to remain sane in the midst of such a large family and adventures in a strange and fascinating land. This is a story filled with tenderness that makes one think about life, about the importance of human relationships, true firendship, and intimacy as an anchor. Little by little, the reader gathers that the wife died in an accident just before they all left Spain, a fact to which the husband cannot resign himself. The language is exquisite and the style impeccable.

▶ *María E. Gentle*   Arlington Public Library

POR el LIBRO.

 Authors: Various **NEW**

This stunning collection of short stories captures the pure joy of reading and the magic of literature. Intended for older readers, incorporating a variety of styles and themes, it combines attractive illustrations with notable, award winning authors from all over Latin America and Spain, including Jesús Ballaz, Yanitzia Canetti, Ricardo Chávez Castañeda, Silvia Dubovoy, Ana María Fernández, Alfredo Gómez Cerdá, Concha López Narváez, Carlos Puerto, and José A. Ramírez Lozano, among others.

▶ *Teresa Mlawer* Lectorum Publications

PRIMAVERA con ESQUINA ROTA.

 Author: Mario Benedetti

An Uruguayan political prisoner longs and hopes to leave prison one day and rejoin his wife and daughter in exile. But life and love follow their course. A great storyteller whose stories absorb the reader, Mario Benedetti offers this beautiful and bittersweet novel.

▶ *Lluís Agustí* Instituto Cervantes New York

PUDOR.

Author: Santiago Roncagliolo **NEW**

One of the most dazzling novels to appear in the world of Spanish literature in recent years, Modesty concerns itself with intimacy and with desires and fears that we dare not say aloud. In this novel, Roncagliolo provides us with a sharp, yet also tender, look on family relations.

▶ *Salvador Vergara* Instituto Cervantes Chicago

LOS que FALSIFICARON la FIRMA de DIOS.

 Author: Viriato Sención

This is a novel of denunciation and a social, political and religious critique which takes place over three decades in a Caribbean city (Santo Domingo). The plot derives its impetus from the corruption and disorder caused by authoritarianism and modern caudillismo, focusing on characters interwoven during a period of a continuing extralegal mandate. The author incorporates magical realist passages, providing a rich touch to the narrative. This novel broke all records for sales in Dominican literary history. It was translated into English after becoming the most sold work during 1993.

▶ *Sarah Aponte* Dominican Studies Institute.CUNY

RAYUELA.

Author: Julio Cortázar

This is an experimental, intellectual, comical and very serious novel that is known for the novelty of its design: one can read the novel straight through, or follow the author's suggested order of chapters. Rayuela refers to the game of hopscotch, which the latter reading resembles in format. The novel is anchored in the 1960's and 70's, and follows an Argentine's life in Paris, and his return to South America. Rayuela was one of the seminal "Boom" literary movement's novels.

▶ *Lynn Shirey*　　　　　　　　　　　　　　　Harvard College Library

EL RECURSO DEL MÉTODO.

Author: Alejo Carpentier

Internationally acclaimed writer Alejo Carpentier gives us this telling of the story of a dictator of an unnamed country in Latin America (could be Cuba, Dominican Republic, Paraguay) and how he deals with conspiracies, a student uprising engineered by the communists, and denies the subjugated peasantry of even their humble status in his society.

▶ *Alina San Juan*　　　　　　　　　　　　　Trade Comission of Spain

LA REGENTA.

Author: Leopoldo Alas "Clarín"

One of the great novels of the 19th century which vividly transports us to the world of the small city, prisoner of religious conditioning and social class barriers. La Regenta is one of the most enchanting female characters in Spanish literature, richly detailed and full of psychological subtlety, and proceeding from a world and time when feminine passion dare not speak its name.

▶ *Elvira Lindo*　　　　　　　　　　　　　　　Writer and Journalist

La Reina del Sur.

Author: Arturo Pérez-Reverte

The protagonist is a woman called Teresa Mendoza, the girlfriend of an apparent drug trafficker (later we discover he was a DEA agent). She has led a difficult life. Then her boyfriend is killed and she knows she has to flee. A "friend" counsels her to hide in Spain and she decides to head south to Morocco. There she meets Santiago, a Galician who teaches her the business of trafficking in hashish, weapons, tobacco, etc. After Santiago's death, Teresa spends a year in prison, where she meets Patty O'Farrell, with whom–after both have been released–she establishes a good cocaine trafficking business. She makes deals with Italians and Russians and becomes a millionaire. We are told of her romances, triumphs, and deceptions. She returns to Mexico, she testifies against those who tried to hurt her, and then she disappears. The language is incredibly realistic and full of Mexican and Spanish slang. The music of narcocorridos and rancheras permeates the entire novel (in fact, the chapter titles are either song titles or lyrics from the same). The novel is immersed in popular culture and in the demimonde of the two continents (actually, three continents). The action is recounted from the perspective of an unnamed journalist, who functions as an omniscient narrator who knows all the details of her life.

▶   *María E. Gentle*   Arlington Public Library

La Reina Isabel Cantaba Rancheras.

Author: Hernán Rivera Letelier
                                                                  NEW

La Reina Isabel cantaba rancheras is probably the best known work by this Chilean writer, who until he was eleven years old, lived in small saltpeter mining towns in northern Chile, and thereafter moved to the city of Antofagasta, where he worked at a variety of jobs. He started writing poetry and short stories, and later devoted himself to novels that are characterized by their forceful and expressive originality, and populated by highly realistic characters. He is a two-time winner (1994 and 1996) of the National Book Council Prize. In 2010 he was awarded the Alfaguara Prize for his novel El arte de la resurrección. He is currently one of the most widely-read writers in Chile.

▶   *María E. Gentle*   Arlington Public Library

El Reinado de Witiza.

Author: Francisco García Pavón
                                                                  NEW

The cases of Tomelloso's chief of municipal police, Plinio, constitute another clear entry in the genre of the Spanish crime thriller. In this novel, one of a series, García Pavón relies on local color to present a critical portrait of society as perceived from the rural settings of the obscurantist Spain of the late Franco era.

▶   *Paloma Graciani*   Biblioteca "José Emilio Pacheco"

EL REINO DE ESTE MUNDO.

Author: Alejo Carpentier

The Kingdom of this World is one of those books which capture and amaze you in a real and marvelous world which will not let you be until you have read each and every one of its pages.

▶ *Paloma Celis Carbajal* — UW-Madison

RÉQUIEM POR UN CAMPESINO ESPAÑOL.

Author: Ramón J. Sender

In Aragon, Mosén Millán, a village priest, prepares to officiate a mass for the soul of Paco el Molinero, a village youth executed in the first days of the Civil War because of his progressive ideas. The priest had baptized the young man, had educated him, and had even chosen him to be his altar boy. When Paco is forced to go into hiding, after the political events which precipitated the war, Mosén Millán, wishing to help the young man, urges him to give himself up. Paco is sentenced to the firing squad, and the priest will be obliged to hear his confession before the execution.

▶ *Lluís Agustí* — Instituto Cervantes New York

RESPIRACIÓN ARTIFICIAL.

Author: Ricardo Piglia

In the novel Respiración artificial a group of friends discuss Argentine literature and writers. It's a wonder for two reasons: on the one hand, it vindicates the coffeehouse model, rather than the academy, as the natural forum to discuss those subjects, and on the other, it criticizes officially consecrated high priests with great wisdom and humor.

▶ *Silvia Gil de Cwilich* — Artist and Reader

REUNIÓN DE CUENTOS.

Author: Jesús Gardea

The recently late Mexican writer Jesús Gardea (1939-2000) stands out in the panorama of Mexican letters by his idiosyncratic use of the Spanish language, by means of which he creates a self-contained universe developed in the course of several novels. Following the trail blazed by Guimaraes Rosa and Lezama Lima, Gardea, in the short stories collected in this volume, concentrates the essential traits of the narrator's craft, striking a balance between the most rigorous control of language and the greatest of imaginative liberties.

▶ *Gaspar Orozco* — Mexican Poet and Diplomat

LOS RÍOS PROFUNDOS.

 Author: José María Arguedas

The beauty and the violence which the young narrator encounters in his travels throughout the Andes are portrayed with tenderness and deep understanding in this autobiographical novel.

▶　*Richard Heyer*　　　　　　　　　　　Instituto Cervantes New York

LOS ROJOS DE ULTRAMAR.

 Author: Jordi Soler

In this cross of memoir, historical document and novel, Mexican writer Jordi Soler, grandson of Republican Spaniards, tells the story of his grandfather Arcadi's arrival in the country and of the founding of a community of exiled Catalans in the middle of the Veracruzan forest. The objective of the community is not just survival as individuals or as a group, more than mere survival, what moves the group is the idea of return.

▶　*Lluís Agustí*　　　　　　　　　　　　Instituto Cervantes New York

ROSARIO TIJERAS.

 Author: Jorge Franco

Story told from the point of view of a young man about his love for an assassin in Medellin, Colombia. Rosario loves Emilio but confides in Pacero. The latter recounts the friendship of the threesome, while Rosario lies dying in a hospital bed after being shot.

▶　*Scott Van Jacob*　　　　　　　　　　University of Notre Dame

EL RUFIÁN MOLDAVO.

 Author: Edgardo Cozarinsky

During the first half of 20th century, Argentina harbored a Jewish criminal organization called Zwi Migdal. This mafia style organization was formed by Jewish procurers who recruited young Jewish women from Russia, Galicia, and other parts of Eastern Europe to be prostitutes throughout Argentina. The Jewish community rejected outright, in life and in death, both the members of Zwi Migdal and their victims. An Argentine residing in Paris, and descendant of artists in Buenos Aires Yiddish theater of that time, repeats and closes a family circle without knowing it. A portentous narrative from the Argentine filmmaker and writer Edgardo Cozarinsky, and stroke of luck for those who not yet read the novel.

▶　*Lluís Agustí*　　　　　　　　　　　　Instituto Cervantes New York

SAB.

Author: Gertrudis Gómez de Avellaneda

NEW

This is one of the most outstanding novels about slavery written in the 19th century. Romantic in both style and atmosphere, this is indispensable reading to learn about the narrative of the period.

▶ *Robert Zaman*   US Librarian

LA SAGA / FUGA DE J.B.

Author: Gonzalo Torrente Ballester

NEW

Nobel Prize winner José Saramago remarked of this work: "until now there was an empty chair to the right of Cervantes, which has just been occupied by Gonzalo Torrente Ballester upon writing "La saga/fuga de J.B." With this experimental novel, Torrente Ballester is able to submerge the reader in one of the most passionate of reading adventures. Torrente Ballester was awarded the Cervantes Prize in 1985.

▶ *Salvador Vergara*   Instituto Cervantes Chicago

SAN MANUEL BUENO MÁRTIR.

Author: Miguel de Unamuno

For those who believe, for those who want to believe and for those who no longer believe, Unamuno's novel will challenge all and force them to rethink their faith.

▶ *Adan Griego*   Stanford University Libraries

SEMBLANZAS DEL CORAZÓN.

Author: José Rafael Lantigua

Semblanzas inscribes past events and experiences into the present collective memory, evoking in nostalgic episodes of what the Dominican town of Moca represented in the past. Lantigua pays homage to the many men and women who contributed to the social and human formation of the mocano of today.

▶ *Nashieli Marcano*   University of Akron

EL SEÑOR PRESIDENTE.

 Author: Miguel Angel Asturias

Guatemalan writer Miguel Ángel Asturias, winner of the Nobel Prize in Literature, is the author of El señor Presidente, an outstanding novel about a Latin American tyrant. Sadly, this literary tradition has been explored by Spanish-language authors because the character recurs so often. The best-known works in this genre are Yo, el Supremo, by Augusto Roa Bastos, El recurso del método, by Alejo Carpentier, and more recently La Fiesta del Chivo, by Mario Vargas Llosa. This book by Miguel Ángel Asturias—based on the figure of the Guatemalan dictator Manuel Estrada Cabrera—is particularly notable because it is one of the first works in this area, and it has a strength and vigor that remain fresh today.

▶ *Lluís Agustí*   Instituto Cervantes New York

SI TE DICEN QUE CAÍ.

 Author: Juan Marsé

One of the fundamental works of modern fiction written in Spain, which placed the Spanish novel in the top echelons of 20th century prose in any language, after the breakdown brought on by the Civil War. The perfect marriage between bold language and likable characters, born in the alleyways produced by the war, make this an indispensable novel in the history of our literature.

▶ *Ernesto Pérez Zúñiga*   Instituto Cervantes

LOS SIETE HIJOS DE SIMENÓN.

NEW

 Author: Ramón Díaz Eterovic

Heredia, a classic detective, of the stature of a Marlowe or Spade, marginal, solitary, enlightened, and skeptical, is charged with investigating the murder of an important lawyer, a crime that, as in all good novels of the genre, unveils a series of political and economic interests. His partner is a cat named after a writer of crime thrillers. The background is an exciting urban fresco depicting the hidden social reality and corruption of Chile in the last few decades.

▶ *Paloma Graciani*   Biblioteca "José Emilio Pacheco"

EL SIGLO DE LAS LUCES.

Author: Alejo Carpentier

Through Victor Hughes we follow the impact of the French Revolution in the Antilles, where the inhabitants dreamed of freedom while the guillotine casts its deadly shadow. A novel that can be identified as a true representative of magic realism, and which gives the reader a comprehensive portrait of the atmosphere surrounding the Age of Enlightment.

Alina San Juan   Trade Comission of Spain

SIN TI NO SOY YO.

Author: Lourdes Vázquez

It is a story of pleasures and tragedies with "espiritismo" and "santería" as backdrop, set in mid-20th century Puerto Rico. The characters, bound by family ties, are taken into a whirlpool of emotions and passions, which as a result, constructs their collective reality.

Nashieli Marcano   University of Akron

SOLDADOS DE SALAMINA.

Author: Javier Cercas

Rafael Sánchez Mazas was a well-known Spanish Falangist writer and politician who was captured by the Republican government during the Civil War. During the final withdrawal of the army to the French border, he was taken before a firing squad and seemed certain to die. The research undertaken by an academic to clarify the elements of this story, becomes a search to discover the identity of the soldier who saved Sánchez Mazas from certain death, and more importantly, to discover his purpose for doing so. An extraordinary work about heroism, love, the passage of time and the recovery of the memories of the disappeared.

Lluís Agustí   Instituto Cervantes New York

SOLDADOS.

Author: Francisco González Ledesma

While some of his works were censored in Spain during the Franco period, Spanish journalist and novelist Francisco González Ledesma was financially forced to produce a Western novella per week under the pseudonym of Silver Kane. From the journalist's trade, which requires the constant and forced exercise of telling stories, there emerged an authentic writer, whose style is clear, precise, relevant and highly evocative. Moreover, González Ledesma is faithful to his people and to his humble origins. Soldados is the story of the three old men from those old neighborhoods, who at the end of their lives and for different reasons —curiosity, vengeance or desperation— start off together on a search.

Lluís Agustí   Instituto Cervantes New York

SOLITUD.

 Author: Víctor Català, pseud. de Caterina Albert

The best novel inspired by Catalan Modernism, and an authentic precursor of the women's literature which would play such an important role in the Catalan literary world.

▶ *Jaume Martí Olivella*   University of New Hampshire

SÓLO CENIZAS HALLARÁS (BOLERO).

Author: Pedro Vergés

This novel reflects Dominican society in the years following the death of dictator Rafael Trujillo (1961-1962). The characters' lives mirror the great economic and socio-cultural changes the country was undergoing at that time. The phenomenon of immigration to the United States is analyzed through the character of Freddy and Yolanda. Freddy represents the young Dominican who sees immigration as the solution to all his financial troubles. Yolanda represents the young woman without much motivation who returns to live in Santo Domingo (the capital of the Dominican Republic) and who faces the problems of adaptation and acclimatization. Vergés presents us with a social novel of daily life in simple language, the language of the barrio, of a people.

▶ *Sarah Aponte*   Dominican Studies Institute. CUNY

SOLO UN MUERTO MÁS.

NEW

Author: Ramiro Pinilla

Veteran writer Ramiro Pinilla pays his own particular homage to the detective novels he so enjoyed in his youth, with an adaptation of the universal archetypes and the classic plot of the crime thriller, transposed to post Civil War Spain in a small village of the Basque country.

▶ *Paloma Graciani*   Biblioteca "José Emilio Pacheco"

LA SOMBRA DE LO QUE FUIMOS.

NEW

Author: Luis Sepúlveda

Three aging revolutionaries exiled after the Pinochet coup go then to plot one last act together.

▶ *Lucía Acosta*   Princeton Public Library

LA SOMBRA DEL VIENTO.

Author: Carlos Ruiz Zafón

One morning in 1945 a boy is taken by his father to a mysterious hidden place in the heart of the old city of Barcelona: The Cemetery of Forgotten Books. There Daniel Sempere discovers a book which will change the course of his life and will lead him to a labyrinth of intrigue and secrets hidden in the dark soul of the city.

▶ *María Casado*   Miami Dade College

SON DE MAR.

Author: Manuel Vicent

This is a beautiful novel written with a magnificent prose yet easy to read. Manuel Vicent won with this book the Alfaguara prize in 1999.

▶ *Alvaro Sanabria*   San Francisco Public Library

LA SONRISA ETRUSCA.

Author: José Luis Sampedro

At the end of his life, sick and lonely, an old Italian fighter spends his last days in the company of his daughter and grandson in a Northern Italian city. A beautiful work about the meaning of life, memories, friendship and love.

▶ *Lluís Agustí*   Instituto Cervantes New York

SOY CAMPEÓN.

Author: Dinorah Coronado

NEW

The book is a historical novel based on the author's father, a Dominican Republic "Olympian" racer of very humble origins. It shows how he cultivated his skills and inculcated them.

▶ *Nellie B. Mulkay*   N Y State Spanish Bilingual Education Technical Assistance Center at NYU

LOS SUEÑOS DE LOS HOMBRES SE LOS FUMAN LAS MUJERES.

Author: Alister Ramírez Márquez

NEW

Tells the story of two Colombian immigrants who come to New York at the end of 19th century. Hans and Pedronel, the protagonists, love adventures, and their lives will change forever when they meet Virginia.

▶ *Nellie B. Mulkay*   N Y State Spanish Bilingual Education Technical Assistance Center at NYU

SUEÑOS Y DISCURSOS.

Author: Francisco de Quevedo

The Sueños consist of five visions of hell, visited by the author in his dreams. He encounters people of various social classes and professions being punished for their sins and lampoons them hasrshly with his mordant wit. This work is both the bitterest and most amusing satire of the Golden Age.

▶   *Eduardo de Lamadrid*   Trans-Lingual Communications Inc.

EL SUR; SEGUIDO DE BENE.

Author: Adelaida García Morales

A novel about a young Spanish woman's memories of her childhood in Sevilla, which prove to be erroneous.

▶   *Lynn Shirey*   Harvard College Library

TE DI LA VIDA ENTERA.

Author: : Zoe Valdés

NEW

At the beginning of the novel, the heroine commits herself totally to "the man of her life" and when he abandons her in 1959, she directs her commitment to the Revolution, victorious that very year. Thus begins this story of devotion and disillusion.

▶   *Rafael E. Tarrago*   University of Minnesota

TENGO MIEDO TORERO.

Author: Pedro Lemebel

Lemebel, the "enfant terrible" of current Chilean writing, had been writing on the "margins" during the Pinochet dictatorship. His text captures with much wit that tragic time for his country with the voice of some one who has endured that tragedy for not conforming to the norm. When asked once, if he wanted to play with dolls as a child, he noted, "I wanted to be the doll!" That's the beauty of Lemebel's narrative, recently translated into English as My Tender Matador.

▶   *Adan Griego*   Stanford University Libraries

TERRAZO.

Author: Abelardo Díaz Alfaro

This highly acclaimed short-story collection by Díaz Alfaro encompasses the struggle of the islanders in rural Puerto Rico, engaging in a lyrical language when describing the countryside landscape.

▶ *Nashieli Marcano*　　　　　　　　　　　　　　　University of Akron

TESIS DE UN HOMICIDIO.

Author: Diego Paszkowski

Paul, the aristocratic son of an Argentine diplomat in France, travels to Buenos Aires to take a course in Criminal Law. There we encounter Paul's professor, who witnesses a crime right in front of the office of the School of Law. He suspects one of his students and becomes obsessed with finding him. Concomitantly, Paul becomes obsessed with an actress, for whom he searches in all women. A cinematographic novel and impossible to put down.

▶ *Martha Berman*　　　　　　　　Professor of Language and Literature

EL TESTIGO.

Author: Juan Villoro

The first classic novel to appear in Mexico after the political changes, The Witness offers the reader a fully realized panorama of a country in which the vestiges and phantoms of the past coexist daily with the wounds of a schizophrenic and convulsive present. Under a climate which has reached a boiling point, Juan Villoro (1956) relates in a precise and intelligent style the odyssey of a Mexican professor who returns to his native land after a long absence. As in the Homeric epic, he discovers that the return to Ithaca is impossible.

▶ *Paloma Graciani*　　　　　　　　Biblioteca "José Emilio Pacheco"

LA TÍA JULIA Y EL ESCRIBIDOR.

Author: Mario Vargas Llosa

NEW

The skillful structure of this novel, written by one of the classic authors of the so-called Latin American boom, moves expertly between literary discourse and that of the radionovela, a popular genre which forms an important part of Latin American culture, and which is here expressed in unexpected literary flights.

▶ *Octavio Núñez*　　　　　　　　　　　　　　　US Librarian

EL TIEMPO DE LOS EMPERADORES EXTRAÑOS.

NEW

Author: Ignacio del Valle

Leningrad, 1943 is the setting for this historical work where crimes infused with Masonic rituals, intrigues by the military, and the war are the perfect ingredients of a story with the structure and characters of the classic crime thriller.

▶ *Paloma Graciani*   Biblioteca "José Emilio Pacheco"

TIRANT LO BLANC.

Author: Joanot Martorell

The fundamental novel of medieval Catalan literature and the first modern novel in the critical consideration of Mario Vargas Llosa.

▶ *Jaume Martí Olivella*   University of New Hampshire

TODOS LOS CUENTOS.

NEW

Author: Cristina Fernández Cubas

An anthology of short stories written by Cristina Fernández Cubas, one of the most prominent Spanish short fiction authors, whose work encompasses three decades, from the Post- Franco 80's to the present. This anthology compiles her five published books: Mi hermana Elba, Los altillos de Brumal, El ángulo del horror, Con Agatha en Estambul, and Parientes pobres del diablo. It also includes an unpublished short story, "El faro (The Lighthouse)" which continues an unfinished short story by Edgar Allan Poe of the same title. Her stories, tinged with an intense and precise prose, seamlessly integrate unexpected and mysterious elements into the account of everyday life. Some of her short stories have been translated into English and published in journals.

▶ *Jesús Alonso Regalado*   University of Albany

TRAVESURAS DE LA NIÑA MALA.

Author: Mario Vargas Llosa

A adolescent in Lima falls in love with a girl when she moves in to his privileged neighborhood. The girl disappears when the story she gave of her life proved to be false, but reappears, as a women, in the life of the protagonist when he is a man in Paris. Thus begins this fascinating story of love, dedication, and deracination.

▶ *Rafael E. Tarrago*   University of Minnesota

EL TREN PASA PRIMERO.

Author: Elena Poniatowska

Poniatowska should be on an essential list. She is well-known for her journalism and political commentary in Mexico. This is a novel about the railroad movement in Mexico acclaimed at the Guadalajara Book Fair.

► *Millie Torrance*   Sacramento Public Library

TRES TRISTES TIGRES.

Author: Guillermo Cabrera Infante

An unclassifiable book, a conjunction of journalistic, literary and cinematographic techniques, it constitutes a unique case in Hispanic literature. An immense play on words elevated to the category of great literature which proved extremely influential in Latin America.

► *Fernando Velázquez Medina*   Writer and Journalist

TRILOGÍA SUCIA DE LA HABANA.

Author: Pedro Juan Gutiérrez

Written in strong and aggressive language, which is almost a kick in the chest to the reader, this is a collection of three stories, which resemble, by their unity of style and characterization, an experimental novel. A best seller which is, above all, good literature.

► *Fernando Velázquez Medina*   Writer and Journalist

TRÍPTICO DEL MAL:
SEÑAS DE IDENTIDAD; DON JULIÁN ; JUAN SIN TIERRA.

Author: Juan Goytisolo NEW

Regarded as one of the greatest living Spanish novelists (though he now lives in self-exile in Morocco), this tríptico (or triptych) – name later given to the trilogy by the publisher El Aleph Editores in 2004 – may be Goytisolo's most challenging and mystifying achievement. Also known as the Álvaro Mendiola trilogy, it comprises three novels: Señas de identidad (Marks of Identity, 1966), Reivindicación del conde don Julián (Count Julian, 1970), and Juan sin tierra (1975). Because of their subversive nature, all three were banned in Spain until after Franco's death. Originally published in 1975 by Seix Barral, Juan sin tierra was revised by Goytisolo in 2006. Together, they are a categorical rejection of Spain's past and celebration of the power of writing through his self-reflexive narration and a postmodern protagonist named Julián, the great traitor and count of Ceuta.

► *Claude Potts*   University of California

TRISTE, SOLITARIO Y FINAL.

 Author: Osvaldo Soriano   NEW

This first novel by this journalist and writer reveals a perfect combination of the epic and a sense of humor. The novel is a homage to the classic crime novel (the title is a quotation from The Long Goodbye) and at the same time an outrageous tragicomedy that combines tears and laughter, actors and characters, reality and fiction.

▶ *Paloma Graciani*   Biblioteca "José Emilio Pacheco"

TU ROSTRO MAÑANA.

 Author: Javier Marías   NEW

This is Javier Marías' most ambitious work. Composed as a trilogy, the story which evolves in more than one thousand six hundred pages, is demanding and difficult, but well worth the reader's effort. In this work, we again find elements and characters which have appeared in other novels by Marías, places and settings are reprised, but they remain enthralling all the same. Marías should occupy a place in every library that concerns itself with Spanish literature.

▶ *Salvador Vergara*   Instituto Cervantes Chicago

EL TÚNEL.

 Author: Ernesto Sábato   NEW

The Argentine writer Ernesto Sábato published The Tunnel in 1948 and shortly thereafter it was recognized as one of the fundamental novels of Argentine literature. Pessimistic in tone, the novel narrates the story of a murder and an obsession. Ernesto Sábato was awarded the Cervantes Prize in 1984.

▶ *Salvador Vergara*   Instituto Cervantes Chicago

TUYO ES EL REINO.

 Author: Abilio Estévez

Acclaimed by European critics, The New York Times and readers, Abilio Estévez's first novel won the Prize for the best foreign novel published in France in 2000. A work that surely would have been praised by Virgilio Piñera, mentor and teacher of Abilio Estévez.

▶ *Fernando Velázquez Medina*   Writer and Journalist

LA ÚLTIMA NIEBLA.

NEW

Author: María Luisa Bombal

Another fundamental work of literature by a woman from the Americas. An object of studies and thesis in numerous universities in America and Europe.

▶ *Octavio Núñez*   US Librarian

LA ÚLTIMA NOCHE de DOSTOIEVSKI.

Author: Cristina Peri Rossi

A player narrates a life of regrets, as he confronts his obsession with the help of a psychologist.

▶ *Scott Van Jacob*   University of Notre Dame

EL ÚLTIMO CATÓN.

Author: Matilde Asensi

This is a perfect book for readers who have enjoyed the novels of Dan Brown and Umberto Eco. However, this book was published before The Da Vinci Code and perhaps Dan Brown is in the debt of this marvelous author.

▶ *Gabriel Partlow*   Pima County Public Library

UN MUNDO para JULIUS.

Author: Alfredo Bryce Echenique

NEW

The world of Julius, a child of privilege growing up in a bourgoise family in Lima, is portrayed with great humor and tenderness. As the youngest in the family he is spoiled by both his family and the servants, but as he gets older he comes to see the deep conflict that exists between those two worlds.

▶ *Richard Heyer*   Biblioteca "Jorge Luis Borges"

UNA PALABRA TUYA.

Author: Elvira Lindo

Winner of the Biblioteca Breve Prize, Una palabra tuya narrates the story of a woman who's dissatisfied with the evolution of her life, work, friends and love relationships. Although Elvira Lindo is perhaps best known for her comical children's books, and for the multiple registries her language assumes taken from popular and everyday speech, in this novel she displays a superior command of language to describe and share pain, to narrate the epic of normal lives, and to show the human tragedy, of taking final responsibility for one's own happiness.

▶ *Lluís Agustí*   Instituto Cervantes New York

EL UNICORNIO.

Author: Manuel Mujica Lainez

NEW

This novel with a historical-mythological hew, recreates the medieval world as few other novels penned in Spanish have.

▶ *Octavio Núñez*　　　　　　　　　　　　　　　　　US Librarian

LA VERDAD sobre el CASO SAVOLTA.

Author: Eduardo Mendoza

NEW

We could say that Mendoza starts to configure the genre with this story, written in the code of a crime thriller, about the assassination of the Catalan industrialist Savolta, an arms dealer during World War I . With a magisterial sense of humor and irony, Mendoza presents a corrosive analysis of the economic, political, and social reality of a Barcelona in which a reactionary bourgeousie and a liberal middle class coexist uneasily with a potent worker's and anarchist movement.

▶ *Paloma Graciani*　　　　　　　　　　Biblioteca "José Emilio Pacheco"

LA VIDA del BUSCÓN.

Author: Francisco de Quevedo

This brilliant and cynical novel, supposedly containing many autobiographical episodes, and set in a boarding house in Salamanca peopled by unsavory characters, is one of the wittiest books ever written in Spanish, so packed with conceits and double meanings that it is all but impossible to translate.

▶ *Eduardo de Lamadrid*　　　　　　Trans-Lingual Communications Inc.

LA VIDA EXAGERADA de MARTÍN ROMAÑA.

Author: Alfredo Bryce Echenique

Pinnacle of what some critics have called the new sentimental novel, this work, informed in part by certain topoi of the picaresque novel, presents one of the most likeable and delicious characters in Spanish 20th century literature. Martin Romaña exemplifies a new form of masculinity, which involves tenderness, the profusion of sentiment, verbal play and an uncontainable and fascinating sense of humor.

▶ *Ernesto Pérez Zúñiga*　　　　　　　　　　　　Instituto Cervantes

LA VIDA PERRA DE JUANITA NARBONI.

Author: Angel Vázquez

There was a time during the 20th century in Spain when certain monarchs, dictators, politicians and military officers dreamt of once again gilding coats of arms, some businessmen saw an opportunity, and many Spaniards gave their blood. After the loss of the empire in 1898, the sad 20th century campaigns in Morocco were an attempt to reorganize the dream in African land. After the army came the colonizers in search of hope. A considerable number of Spaniards settled in Tetouan, Larache or Tangier, international city occupied by Franco during the World War II, in this way creating a peculiar culture, apparently Spanish but sharing other indigenous and colonial traits. With the independence of Morocco in 1956 comes the diaspora, the fracture of the dream to which some cling, like Juanita Narboni. The essential novel about Tangier.

▶ *Lluís Agustí*   Instituto Cervantes New York

EL VIENTO DE LA LUNA.

Author: Antonio Muñoz Molina

The Moon Wind recounts the life of a provincial adolescent in Francoist Spain during a week of the month of July 1969. While man is walking on the moon, the adolescent lives in a world anchored in the earth. In this constricted world, he discovers the reality of life, society, and sex, the weight of his being and of those who surround him, loyalty and his father's worth. Magisterially narrated by one of the best contemporary Spanish writers.

▶ *Lluís Agustí*   Instituto Cervantes New York

LA VORÁGINE.

Author: José Eustaquio Rivera

La vorágine is one of the most important and interesting works in Colombian literature, and indeed of Latin American literature as a whole during the first half of the 20th century. The novel's denunciation of the working conditions of Colombian rubber tappers in the jungle is its starting point but not its final result. La vorágine has served as an inspiration and a reinterpretation for an entire generation of Spanish American novelists.

▶ *Lluís Agustí*   Instituto Cervantes New York

LA VERDAD SOSPECHOSA.

Author: Juan Ruiz de Alarcón

The bow-legged and hunchbacked Ruiz de Alarcón was the 17th century's greatest writer of thesis plays and had a great influence on Corneille, Molière and Goldoni. His forte was the development of character types that represent vices and illustrate moral truths. La verdad sospechosa inveighs against the vice of lying, while combining entertainment with ethical teaching. Alarcón was the most modern of his contemporaries and the greatest moralist of the Spanish classical theater.

▶ *Eduardo de Lamadrid*   Trans-Lingual Communications Inc.

EL VUELO DE LA REINA.

Author: Tomás Eloy Martínez

An amazing book about the obsession that well known publisher Camargo has for a young reporter Remis. The political events of Argentina are intertwined in this intriguing story also about power and control. I was intrigued and scared by Camargo and his seemingly dual personality. His sexual voyeurism was both fascinating and revolting. This book won the Premio Alfaguara in 2002.

▶ *Millie Torrance*   Sacramento Public Library

YO EL SUPREMO.

Author: Augusto Roa Bastos

Paraguayan novelist and poet, Augusto Antonio Roa Bastos, who received the Cervantes Prize in letters in 1989, recounts in this modern Latin American classic and masterpiece, the imagined life of the last royal governor voted dictator, Gaspar Rodríguez de Francia while covering more than 100 years of Paraguayan history.

▶ *Libbhy Romero*   Brooklyn Public Library

YO ME PERDONO.

Author: Fietta Jarque

The cultural and religious shock experienced by colonial Peru is manifested in the mestizo art of the Cuzco school and in the lives of four men: a young painter, an Indian, a priest, and a businessman who unite to make the church of Andahuaylillas a center of religious power.

▶ *Richard Heyer*   Instituto Cervantes New York

NON FICTION

LOS 1001 AÑOS de la LENGUA ESPAÑOLA.

Author: Antonio Alatorre

How was our language born? How did it expand? How has it diversified? Alatorre answers these and other questions by narrating the history of Spanish language in an approachable style and using simple language. This book provides us with elements that allow us to understand the language's origins and to follow its development. And as the author says, to share in the magic of its history.

▶ *Paloma Celis Carbajal*   UW-Madison

AHÍ VIENE el LOBO GRIS.

Author: Emma Romeu

NEW

Wolves are strong, fierce, and cunning, but they are also playful and affectionate. This book provides information about the behavior of these wonderful animals and will teach how wolves became endangered and how people are working to save them.

▶ *Nellie B. Mulkay*   N Y State Spanish Bilingual Education Technical Assistance Center at NYU

LA ARAUCANA.

Author: Alonso de Ercilla

NEW

An epic poem which relates the events of the first stage of the Arauco War between the Spanish and the Mapuches in the General Captaincy of Chile. This is the first work of highbrow literature dedicated to an American subject, since Ercilla, in contrast to the average Conquistador, was very well-educated. However, in spite of his artistic ambitions, the author was a participant in the conflict, and his chronicle of the conflict remains the most reliable first-hand account of the events.

▶ *Paloma Graciani*   Biblioteca "José Emilio Pacheco"

EL ARGUMENTO de la OBRA:
CORRESPONDENCIA (1951-1989).

Author: Jaime Gil de Biedma

NEW

Correspondence by Jaime Gil de Biedma between 1959-1989, covering the awaking of his poetical inspirations to his last months of life. This book serves as an intellectual biography of the author throughout different period of his life in Paris, Oxford, Manila and Spain.

▶ *Patricia Figueroa*   Brown University

ARTÍCULOS.

Author: Mariano José de Larra

At the beginning of the convulsive and dramatic 19th century in Spain, a young writer laments the state of his sad, outmoded, uncultured country. The modern style and relevance of Mariano José de Larra's prose, in contrast to many of his contemporaries, is characterized by its precision, rhythm, humor and absence of pomposity. The marvelous journalistic chronicles of the young Larra, who died at the tender age of 27, allows us to approach the way of life and the problems of Spain in the 1830's, some of which are still with us to this day.

▶ *Lluís Agustí*   Instituto Cervantes New York

LA BIEN PLANTADA.

Author: Eugeni d'Ors

Conceived as a philosophical novel, La Ben Plantada, published as a set of marginal notes in 1911, is the magnum opus of the most incisive and important Catalan intellectual of all time. In this work, Xenius, known to the Spanish reader for some of his famous marginal notes, describes the ideal of "Noucentisme" and his particular of vision of Catalonia personified in Teresa, a woman of semi-divine aspect and Greek-Mediterranean aesthetic, who incarnates the concepts of prudence, virtue and seductive and asexual discretion advocated by its author. A masterpiece which, unfortunately, has not been sufficiently appreciated, especially in Catalonia.

▶ *Bernat Dedéu*   Cadena Ser

BIOGRAFÍA DE UN CIMARRÓN.

Author: Miguel Barnet

A disciple of Fernando Ortiz, Miguel Barnet makes an important contribution to the ethnographic literature of the Caribbean with this work, which has received international acclaim. In this biography, Esteban Montejo, a slave who managed to escape from the clutches of the odious "peculiar" institution, recounts his life and describes, perhaps without realizing it, Cuban society at the end of the 19th century and the beginning of the 20th century. A work of enormous importance to understand the cultural subtleties of the Hispanic Caribbean.

▶ *Pedro Canó*   Instituto Cervantes New York

BORGES PROFESOR: CURSO DE LITERATURA INGLESA EN LA UNIVERSIDAD DE BUENOS AIRES.

Authors: Martín Arias, and Martín Hadis, eds.

A finely edited compilation of a course given by Borges on English literature, while not focusing on Spanish, does illustrate the way Borges approached the teaching of literature.

▶ *Silvia Gil de Cwilich* — Artist and Reader

BREVE HISTORIA DE LA LITERATURA ESPAÑOLA.

Authors: Carlos Alvar, José Carlos Mainer, and Rosa Navarro.

Spanish university professors Carlos Alvar, José-Carlos Mainer, and Rosa Navarro are probably the greatest living authorities on Spanish literature, its history and criticism. An excellent and indispensable synthesis.

▶ *Lluís Agustí* — Instituto Cervantes New York

BREVÍSIMA RELACIÓN DE LA DESTRUCCIÓN DE LAS INDIAS.

Author: Bartolomé de las Casas

NEW

The description of the abuses and injustices during the Spanish conquest and colonial rule is the best known and most polemical of the works of Las Casas. Writing more as a moralist than a historian, the author tries to show how the supposedly civilized Spanish destroyed the "paradise" they found in the Indies.

▶ *Richard Heyer* — Biblioteca "Jorge Luis Borges"

BUSCANDO UN INCA: IDENTIDAD Y UTOPÍA EN LOS ANDES.

Author: Alberto Flores Galindo

Eleven essays which relate various attempts to find utopias in Peru, from the search for an earthly paradise during the Conquest, through those in the colonial period culminating in Túpac Amaru's rebellion, and concluding in the 20th century with the millenarian guerrilla war carried by the Shining Path.

▶ *Richard Heyer* — Instituto Cervantes New York

CAMPOS DE NÍJAR.

Author: Juan Goytisolo

New agricultural methods and tourism have greatly changed the people and the landscape of the province of Almería. Juan Goytisolo directed his socially acute eye and heart on a land whose people were prisoners of the scarcity of water and a lack of hope, a region which today has become a natural preserve. It's incumbent on us to recall every so often that Spain only recently has ceased being a country characterized by poverty and emigration. Many changes for the good in a relatively short time have altered the essence and the image of a backward and unjust 19th century Spain which was perpetuated thanks to a long-lived dictatorship. A certain economic prosperity, a democracy not without difficulties and the opening of the country to the world are the keys to this radical change. These objectively positive changes in living standards and social freedoms, however, have produced the appearance of all manner of mountebank nouveau riches. When this happens it is good to recourse to recent social literature like Campos de Níjar in order to remember what we were until yesterday.

▷   *Lluís Agustí*   Instituto Cervantes New York

CANCIONERO POPULAR MEXICANO.

Authors: Mario Kuri Aldana, and Vicente Mendoza Martínez

This two-volume edition published by Conaculta contains over one thousand song lyrics, many of them not only popular in Mexico but throughout Latin America and in other parts of the world. It includes biographical information and indexes by genre, authors and first line.

▷   *Alvaro Sanabria*   San Francisco Public Library

CARTAS DE RELACIÓN (1519-1526).

Author: Hernán Cortés

NEW

A collection of five letters addressed to Charles V in which Cortés describes his voyage to Mexico, his arrival at Tenochtitlán, capital of the Aztec empire, and some of the events which resulted in the conquest of Mexico.

▷   *Paloma Graciani*   Biblioteca "José Emilio Pacheco"

▶   NON FICTION

COMENTARIO DE LA ISAGOGÉ DE PORFIRIO.

Author: Averroes

Born Abu-I-Walis Muhammad ibn Ahmad ibn Rusd in Cordoba in 1126, Averroes is the essential author of Hispano-Arabic philosophy and one of the most important commentators of Aristotle in the history of philosophy. Any of his commentaries is to be recommended, although the commentary on the Book of the Compendium Exhibition of Isagogé of Porfirio has received the most critical attention. In this work, Averroes traces the specific axes of his psychology, according to which the soul, as in Aristotle, is the primary faculty and entelechy of the human body. Elsewhere, the philosopher structures a passionate and complex schema of our cognitive activity in the cogitative, estimative, and judicative faculties. In parallel, Averroes committed himself, in what was a fiery polemic in his time, to affirming the existence of an agent of understanding, a capacity for reasoning common to all men and set apart from any reference to the divine, from which each human being develops his specific intelligence, called speculative understanding.

▶ *Bernat Dedéu*   Cadena Ser

COMENTARIOS REALES.

Authors: Garcilaso de la Vega, Inca

Published in 1609, this remains the exemplary text of New World prose of the 16th and early 17th centuries. It introduced the South American world to Spanish readers and provided perspectives of both native inhabitants and privileged witnesses in Peru.

▶ *Isaías Lerner*   CUNY

CÓMO LEER Y ESCRIBIR POESÍA.

Author: Hugo Hiriart

With a confident and pleasant style, the celebrated Mexican novelist and playwright Hugo Hiriart offers a double introduction to poetry and to the Spanish language, addressed in principle to students of Spanish, but which may be enjoyed by all for its freshness, vigor and easily worn erudition. The guide uses key examples to examine poetic meter, rime, genres and themes, culminating with several chapters dedicated to awakening a taste for poetic writing in the reader. The book includes a bilingual dictionary interspersed within the text for English-speaking students. With this volume, Hiriart has created an indispensable guide for North American libraries and bookstores.

▶ *Gaspar Orozco*   Mexican Poet and Diplomat

CONFIESO QUE HE VIVIDO.

Author: Pablo Neruda

This is a remarkable memoir in which Neruda writes about his journeys to exotic places, encounters with famous people and his love of poetry, life, art, nature and obviously his homeland.

▶ *Alvaro Sanabria*   San Francisco Public Library

CONTRAPUNTO CUBANO DEL TABACO Y AZÚCAR.

Author: Fernando Ortiz

NEW

This is an extended essay on tobacco and sugar and the important role they came to play in Cuba. The author describes how in distinct and contrasting ways they both came to dominate economic as well as cultural and social life on the island.

▶ *Richard Heyer*   Biblioteca "Jorge Luis Borges"

CONTRAPUNTO DE GÉNERO Y RAZA EN PUERTO RICO.

Authors: Idsa E. Alegría Ortega, and Palmira N. Ríos, eds.

In light of the 2000 Census, where 85.5% of the population in Puerto Rico identified itself as white, this collection of essays contributes to the race debate by defining racism, its multiple ways of manifestation, its functionality and consequences.These articles pay special attention to the role of the Afro-Puerto Rican woman in the formation of national and international civil society, intersecting race and gender. Some of the topics covered include: history of black women in early 20th century education, racial ideology, Dominican migrant women, the racialization of women's work and national identity.

▶ *Nashieli Marcano*   University of Akron

CONVERSACIÓN ENTRE ESCRITORAS DEL CARIBE HISPANO: TOMO II.

Authors: Daisy Cocco De Filippis, and Sonia Rivera Valdéz, eds.

The essays collected in this volume make an essential reference text for readers interested in the vision of contemporary Caribbean women writers. Conversación covers a wide range of literary genres, such as poetry, short story, novel and children literature, as well as dialogues that allow us to better understand their takes on the literary world.

▶ *Nashieli Marcano*   University of Akron

CRÍTICA Y FICCIÓN.

Author: Ricardo Piglia

Collection of essays covering mostly, but not exclusively Argentine writers. Truly a gem.

▶ *Silvia Gil de Cwilich*   Artist and Reader

CRUZANDO LA FRONTERA: LA CRÓNICA
IMPLACABLE DE UNA FAMILIA MEXICANA QUE EMIGRA A ESTADOS UNIDOS.
Author: Rubén Martínez

Award-winning journalist's poignant depiction of one Mexican family's courageous, multi-generational journey from Michoacán, Mexico to the U.S.

Patricia Cuesta   Los Angeles Public Library

CUADERNOS DE RUSIA.

Author: Dionisio Ridruejo

The politician, intellectual and poet Dionisio Ridruejo was one of the founders of the Spanish Falange, the extreme right revolutionary group which actively participated in the Francoist insurrection. In the recent aftermath of the Civil War, Ridruejo is one of the first voices to register disagreement with the new regime. Ridruejo resigns all his posts and departs for the Russian front with the Blue Division, the Spanish expeditionary force fighting alongside the Germans. In Cuadernos de Rusia he recounts his departure from Spain, his encounter with the Nazi reality and the discovery of Russia, while little by little his principles take other pathways.

Lluís Agustí   Instituto Cervantes New York

CUANDO ERA PUERTORRIQUEÑA.

Author: Esmeralda Santiago

NEW

One of the best coming-of-age stories I've read. Must read for Anglo-Americans to better understand others, specifically, those who have come from Puerto Rico; a part of the US but not.

Stephanie Weiss   University of North Florida Library

CURSO DE REDACCIÓN. TEORÍA Y PRÁCTICA
DE LA COMPOSICIÓN Y DEL ESTILO.
Author: Gonzalo Martín Vivaldi

A great book which helps to resolve questions related to usage as well as to the composition of different types of texts.

Marko Miletich   Binghamton University (SUNY)

EL DARDO EN LA PALABRA.

Author: Fernando Lázaro Carreter

Eminent Spanish language scholar and philologist Fernando Lázaro Carreter wrote a series of newspaper articles under the rubric "The Dart in the Word'. The objective of those articles was to correct usage and abusage of words in journalistic language, a task which at first glance might appear inquisitorial, but which was always effected with rigor, relevance, humor and irony, making those articles a perfect example of the joy of learning. The work recommended is a selection which has the same generic title as the newspaper articles. A second anthology was subsequently published as The New Dart in the Word. An enriching and enjoyable reading experience.

▶ , *Lluís Agustí*   Instituto Cervantes New York

DE CRISTÓBAL COLÓN A FIDEL CASTRO.
EL CARIBE, FRONTERA IMPERIAL.

Author: Juan Bosch

The historical magnum opus of this Dominican intellectual, once president of his country and a politician of great influence among Latin Americans who struggled against the military dictatorships of the 20th century. Juan Bosch sets out with dazzling clarity the history of exploitation suffered by the Caribbean since the arrival of the first Europeans until the triumph of Fidel Castro's bearded guerillas in Cuba. This work is required reading for anyone wishing to learn the history and idiosyncrasy of the Caribbean as a region. The title echoes the work of another outstanding Caribbean figure, English in this case: Eric Williams, anti-colonial fighter and promoter of African independence movements.

▶ *Pedro Canó*   Instituto Cervantes New York

DEL SENTIMIENTO TRÁGICO DE LA VIDA.

Author: Miguel de Unamuno

Essential writer of the Generation of 1898, Unamuno's philosophy is the product of the existential situation of Spain after the loss of its last colonies and describes the challenge of taking the country to an intellectual level comparable with the rest of Europe. The outlines of Del sentimiento trágico de la vida are sketched in insurmountable paradox which exists between the concepts of living and knowing. For Unamuno, human life is characterized by its complete irrationality, an irrationality which places it in irrepressible contradiction with the vital desires for knowledge innate in man. Elsewhere, Unamuno advocates for a complete differentiation between the spheres of reason and sentiment, two facets of the human being which are absolutely irreconcilable. According to Unamuno, life is synonymous with struggle, and more so, the life of an intellectual, a being who finds himself in the center of a struggle between reason and the needs of his appetite and will.

▶ *Bernat Dedéu*   Cadena Ser

EL CUADERNO GRIS.

Author: Josep Pla

In this diary of youth, Catalan journalist Josep Pla (1897-1981) displays the pictorial prose which governed his subsequent prolific work, which extends to more than seventy volumes. Pla would write about the great events of the 20th century with the same aplomb and aversion to overstatement, whether from idealism or grandiloquence, which he evinces at 20 years of age in this work, considered to be his masterpiece.

▶ *Alfons Luna*   AFP New York

EL PEZ EN EL AGUA: MEMORIAS.

Author: Mario Vargas Llosa

Mario Vargas Llosa relates his childhood, adolescent and young adulthood memories, alternating chapter by chapter, with his experiences as a candidate for the presidency of Peru, as well as his justifications for said candidacy. Apart from the brilliant and precise style for which he is known, the work offers the added incentive of discovering those personal experiences which informed novels such as La ciudad y los perros (The City and the Dogs) The Green House (La casa verde), and Aunt Julia and the Scriptwriter (La tía Julia y el escribidor).

▶ *Lluís Agustí*   Instituto Cervantes New York

EL ENSAYO HISPANOAMERICANO DEL SIGLO XX.

Author: John Skirius, ed.

Undergoing consecutive and necessary editions, this anthology has become indispensable and a required recommendation. Among the authors included in this excellent selection of the best 20th century Hispanic-American essays are Alfonso Reyes, Fernando Ortiz, José Carlos Mariategui, Enrique Anderson Imbert, Alejo Carpentier, Octavio Paz and Carlos Monsiváis. A sometimes forgotten genre in Hispanic-American literary histories, but certainly not due to a lack of superior writers and profound works, comparable to the highest essayistic achievements at the international level.

▶ *Lluís Agustí*   Instituto Cervantes New York

ENSEÑAR A TRADUCIR: METODOLOGÍA EN LA FORMACIÓN DE TRADUCTORES E INTÉRPRETES.

Author: Amparo Hurtado Albir

A very practical book which presents a course of study for the teaching of translation.

▶ *Marko Miletich*   Binghamton University (SUNY)

LA ESCLAVITUD DEL NEGRO EN SANTO DOMINGO.

Author: Carlos Esteban Deive

Slave relations in the Spanish colony of Santo Domingo were very different from those which prevailed in great part of the French Caribbean, in the English-speaking Caribbean and in Cuba, until the late abolition of slavery in the largest of the Antilles. The author analyzes those relations with an economic perspective, and as a serious researcher, committed to the exposition of historical truth.

> *Pedro Canó*   Instituto Cervantes New York

ESCRITURAS DE FRIDA KAHLO.

Author: Frida Kahlo

Diego Rivera's personal secretary compiled these very personal and insightful writings by Kahlo on the topic of her private life, her painting, her husband, family and friends.

> *Patricia Cuesta*   Los Angeles Public Library

ESPAÑA EN SU HISTORIA.

Author: Américo Castro
A controversial look at Spanish history.

> *Patricia Figueroa*   Brown University Library

ESPECIALIDADES REGIONALES DE LA COCINA MEXICANA.

Authors: Socorro Puig & María Stoopen

NEW

This impressive cookbook presents the rich diversity of Mexican cooking. Both experts on the topic, the two authors present specialties from all over the republic including Shrimp Pozole from Nayarit, Enchiladas from San Luis Potosi, Fried Corn with Eggs from Morelos, Octopus in its Ink from Campeche, Chicken with Capers from the Yucatan, Mole from Oaxaca, Tripe from Coahuila, and Coconut Rice Pudding from Guerrero. The history of Mexican cooking and a glossary are included for further appreciation of the amazing cuisine.

> *Teresa Mlawer*   Lectorum Publications

FEDERICO GARCÍA LORCA.

Author: Ian Gibson

Certainly the most complete biography of the great Lorca. It is also a biography of Spain at a great time of crisis. Gibson himself revised and translated the English edition published in 1989.

> *Adan Griego*   Stanford University Libraries

LA FLORIDA DEL INCA.

Author: Garcilaso de la Vega
NEW

This is the first chronicle of the Indies written by a mestizo author born in the New World, the son of a Spanish captain and an Inca princess. It narrates the failed expedition (1539-1543) of the explorer Hernando de Soto to the vast and unexplored territory known as La Florida.

▶ *Paloma Graciani*   Biblioteca "José Emilio Pacheco"

FRANCO, CAUDILLO DE ESPAÑA.

Author: Paul Preston

An extensive and well-documented biography of General Francisco Franco, the dictator who governed Spain between 1939 and 1975. An excellent work of historical and political research, as well as a sociological and psychological study of the public and private lives of the Caudillo.

▶ *Lluís Agustí*   Instituto Cervantes New York

GASTRONOMÍA SALUDABLE.

Authors: Rafael Ansón & Gregorio Varela
NEW

Learn how to prepare and enjoy haute cuisine that's healthy and delicious. This book describes the health benefits of a number of foods, explains the food pyramid, and offers complete menus for every season. The recipes include Gluten-Free Bread, Rice with Chicken and Vegetables, Spaghetti Carbonara, Gazpacho, Lentil Stew with Ham and Chorizo, Veal Meatballs, Rabbit with Squash and Fried Potatoes, Grilled Swordfish, and much more.

▶ *Teresa Mlawer*    Lectorum Publications

LA GUIA DE SALUD: CONSEJOS Y RESPUESTAS PARA LA MUJER LATINA.

Author: Jane Delgado
NEW

Excellent, current health information about the major conditions affecting Latinas.

▶ *Barbara Bibel*   Oakland Public Library

HISTORIA DE LOS DESCUBRIMIENTOS DE NUEVA ESPAÑA.

Author: Baltasar Obregón
NEW

Report sent by Baltasar Obregón to the Council of the Indies in 1584. This is a primary source filled with valuable historical and linguistic information, since the author is the first Creole Mexican historian who offers us a vision of the Conquest. Obregón, son of Spaniards, lives his life immersed in the development of the Conquest and is a clear exponent of the society, dreams, and zeitgeist of his age.

▶ *Paloma Graciani*   Biblioteca "José Emilio Pacheco"

HISTORIA de los INDIOS de la NUEVA ESPAÑA (1541).

NEW

Author: Fray Toribio de Benavente (Motolinía)

This work is of special interest because of the author's cultural education as well as his knowledge of the Nahuatl language and his ability to decipher Aztec codexes, thus providing us with first-hand information about and from the Native Americans. This Franciscan friar, who rivals Bartolomé de las Casas in importance, defended the Indians against the abuses committed against them, although he did not condemn forced religious conversion. Even so, his work is an invitation to delve into the wonder of Aztec civilization and the Nahuatl language and etymologies.

▶   *Paloma Graciani*   Biblioteca "José Emilio Pacheco"

HISTORIAS de CLÓSET.

NEW

Author: Claudia Arcila

A welcome addition of serious essays to a much needed and almost non-existent sexuality narratives in Spanish.

▶   *Adan Griego*   Stanford University

HISTORIAS de VERDAD.

NEW

Authors: Various

Historias de Verdad is a wonderfully illustrated collection of books that examines Mexican history from the pre-Hispanic to post-Revolutionary eras. Each book in the eight part series is accessible for young adults who will particularly enjoy margin highlights filled with interesting details and anecdotes written by noted historians.

▶   *Mónica Chapa Domercq*   Oceanside Public Library

LAS HISTORIAS PROHIBIDAS del PULGARCITO.

Author: Roque Dalton

Using Gabriela Mistral's phrase, "El Salvador, America's little thumb." as a point of departure, poet and journalist Roque Dalton creates an absorbing essay about the history and reality of America's little thumb.

▶   *Lluís Agustí*   Instituto Cervantes New York

LA ISLA QUE SE REPITE.

Author: Antonio Benítez Rojo

The author's most outstanding work, it uses essays, narrative, chaos theory and postmodern theory in an attempt to comprehend the Caribbean soul. This unique book dazzled American academics, was praised by John Updike and received the Pushcart Prize.

▷ *Fernando Velázquez Medina*   Writer and Journalist

EL PAÍS DE CUATRO PISOS Y OTROS ENSAYOS.

Author: José Luis González

González delineates the stages of Puerto Rican culture and nation as a reflex of ongoing power relations within the colonial society and under the impact of foreign domination. El país de cuatro pisos is to the 1980's what "Insularismo", the classic essay by Antonio Pedreira, was in the 1930's.

▷ *Nashieli Marcano*   University of Akron

JUAN PÉREZ JOLOTE: BIOGRAFÍA DE UN TZOTZIL.

Author: Ricardo Pozas

This is an ethnological re-creation of the life of a Mexican Tzotzil Indian. A daily account of the life, times and changes of the indigenous.

▷ *Angélica Hurtado Gracia*   Los Angeles Public Library

EL LARGO VIAJE.

Author: Jorge Semprún

Jorge Semprún (1923) lived out his adolescence between two wars, the Spanish Civil War and World War II. Convinced that Hitler's defeat would lead to Franco's fall, this grandson of Prime Minister Antonio Maura, and Minister of Culture between 1988 and 1991, joined the French Resistance, and at 19 years of age was imprisoned in the Buchenwald death camp. His experience there was recounted in The Long Journey (El largo viaje), the best testimony by a Spaniard of the Nazi extermination program.

▷ *Alfons Luna*   AFP New York

LATINOAMÉRICA: SU CIVILIZACIÓN Y SU CULTURA.

Author: Eugenio Chang Rodríguez

This book deals with key historical and cultural events that occurred in Latin America. Each chapter includes comprehension exercises and a bilingual vocabulary.

▷ *Guillermina Raffo Magnasco*   St. Thomas University

LO ESENCIAL en la ORTOGRAFÍA.

 Author: Francisco Alvero Frances

Contains a long list of homophones and a presentation of the principal orthographic rules which govern the use of our consonants.

▶ *Marlenys Villamar* Professor

MANUAL de TRADUCCIÓN Inglés / Castellano.

Authors: Gabriel López Guix, and J. Minnet Wilkinson

A very skillful comparative analysis of the English and Spanish languages which stresses the syntactical, morphological and punctuation aspects of each language.

▶ *Marko Miletich* Binghamton University (SUNY)

MÁS ALLÁ de MI.

 Author: Francisco Jiménez

NEW

The third book in the autobiography series of Mexican author and Professor Francisco Jiménez. This book deals with his college years and his mixed feelings on achieving success against all adversity and the price his family had to pay for his success.

▶ *Odalys Trapote Igneri* New York City Department of Education

MEMORIA de la MELANCOLÍA.

 Author: María Teresa León

María Teresa León recounts her personal, political, cultural and literary experiences. An exquisite novelist of the poetic Generation of 1927, she shared her life with the poet Rafael Alberti, to whom she was also united by literature and political struggle. Memoria de la melancolía is one of the most beautiful prose works ever written about the era of the Republic, the Civil War and exile.

▶ *Lluís Agustí* Instituto Cervantes New York

MEMORIAS.

 Author: Carlos Barral

Carlos Barral was undoubtedly one of the most important Spanish editors of the 20th century, besides being a first-rate reader and critic. A complex and difficult poet, he is however an excellent prose stylist. His memoirs are divided into three volumes: Years of Punishment, which relates his childhood, adolescence and young adulthood in the years following the Civil War; The Inexcusable Years, which relates his experiences during the 1950's; and The Fleeting Hours, which closes the cycle with his mature adult life, with special reference to his cultural and literary life.

▶ *Lluís Agustí*   Instituto Cervantes New York

MISIÓN del BIBLIOTECARIO.
y otros ENSAYOS AFINES.

 Author: José Ortega y Gasset

In the inaugural conference of proceedings of the 11th International Congress of Libraries and Bibliography, celebrated jointly in Madrid and Barcelona in May 1935, Spanish philosopher José Ortega y Gasset gave a lecture, or to be more exact, read his essay The Mission of the Librarian, a text which in spite of the passage of 70 years continues to be of enormous interest and relevance. Required reading for librarians and recommended for all library users.

▶ *Lluís Agustí*   Instituto Cervantes New York

MISS NARCO.

 Author: Javier Valdéz Cárdenas
NEW

Mexican journalist Javier Valdéz Cárdenas offers women's perspectives on the dark and consuming world of narcotics trafficking. Based on a series of interviews, Valdez's vignettes are all at once engrossing, poignant and frightening.

▶ *Mónica Chapa Domercq*   Oceanside Public Library

MITOLOGÍA Y ARTES PREHISPÁNICAS DE LAS ANTILLAS.

Author: José Juan Arrom

José Juan Arrom is one of the most important figures in pre-Hispanic studies in the Caribbean. In this work, his expert eye falls on the relationships between mythology and the arts of the indigenous peoples of the archipelago and explains some of those links.

▷ *Pedro Canó*   Instituto Cervantes New York

MÚSICA DE CINE EN ESPAÑA:
SEÑAS DE IDENTIDAD EN LA BANDA SONORA CONTEMPORÁNEA.

Author: Teresa Fraile Prieto   NEW

Música de cine en España studies the history of Spanish soundtracks during the 1990s and the beginning of the 21st century. It explores various film genres and the characteristics of their respective musical compositions.

▷ *Patricia Figueroa*   Brown University

NAUFRAGIOS Y COMENTARIOS.

Author: Alvar Núñez Cabeza de Vaca

This account of the journeys of Spanish explorer Alvar Núñez Cabeza de Vaca throughout northern North America, and later throughout the southernmost regions of the continent, evinces, beyond its immense historical importance, literary and human merit of the first order. In clear and precise prose, Alvar Núñez details the fortunes (less of these) and misfortunes (more of these) of his wanderings in the almost unfathomable distances of the southern United States and northern Mexico, collecting his incisive observations about the regions and the inhabitants encountered along the way. Naufragios y Comentarios is an eyewitness testimony to one of the great enterprises of the human spirit.

▷ *Gaspar Orozco*   Mexican Poet and Diplomat

▷ NON FICTION

LA NOCHE DE LOS LÁPICES.

 Author: María Seoane

This book is based on the disapearance of several high school students which occurred during the military dictatorship in Argentina in September 1976. Seven high school students, all residing in the city of La Plata, demanded a student fare from the government. The student fare was a reduced fare instituted to help the students reach their schools, but it had since been eliminated by the military government. For such a petition, the students were "disappeared" and tortured. Only one student managed to escape and this book is based on his experiences and his denunciations of what happened in Argentina during the so-called "Dirty War."

▶ *Daniel Berdaner*   Forest Hill Public Library

LA NOCHE DE TLATELOLCO.

 Author: Elena Poniatowska

This book chronicles the events of the student protests in October of 1968 in Mexico City that resulted in the massacre of more than 300 persons.

▶ *Teresa Chapa*   University of North Carolina at Chapel Hill

LA OLA LATINA: CÓMO LOS HISPANOS ESTÁN TRANSFORMANDO LA POLÍTICA EN LOS ESTADOS UNIDOS.

 Author: Jorge Ramos

A powerful, well-documented analysis of why the growing numbers of Latinos in the United States can no longer be ignored and how they are changing the face of the country.

▶ *Patricia Cuesta*   Los Angeles Public Library

ORÁCULO MANUAL Y ARTE DE PRUDENCIA.

 Author: Baltasar Gracián

A collection of 300 aphorisms or maxims about wisdom, by one of the greatest prose stylists in the Spanish language. In them can be discerned a whole plan of conduct for life which, four hundred years later, seems surprisingly modern.

▶ *Eduardo Lago*   Instituto Cervantes New York

LOS ORISHAS EN CUBA.

Author: Natalia Bolívar Aróstegui

For those interested in Afro-Caribbean religions, this book is a must read. The author touches on the entire pantheon of the Cuban divinities-orishas and on her journey leaves us with a fascinating description of the beliefs and aspirations of the faithful. An important work in the field of comparative religion studies.

▶ *Pedro Canó*   Instituto Cervantes New York

PADRE RICO, PADRE POBRE.

Author: Robert T. Kiyosaki
                                                      NEW

This is a financial advice book based on two men with successful careers. Both fathers teach their kids different ways to work, but they both firmly stress education.

▶ *Rafael Pérez Mercado*   Biblioteca Pública Raquel Quiñones

EL PAIS BAJO MI PIEL.

Author: Gioconda Belli

A fascinating autobiography by Nicaragua's most important contemporary writer. Belli chronicles very personal accounts of her life as well as her active participation in the Sandinista revolution.

▶ *Teresa Chapa*   University of North Carolina at Chapel Hill

PALABRAS CRUZADAS.

Author: Gabriel Rolón
                                                      NEW

This self-help book presents the analytic process of the words of a patient who, using pain as an original subject, uncovers a truth capable of changing one's life forever.

▶ *Rafael Pérez Mercado*   Biblioteca Pública Raquel Quiñones

PAULA.

Author: Isabel Allende   **NEW**

This autobiographical memoir is admirably well-written, and in my opinion, after the previous novel, is the author's best work.

▶ *Robert Zaman*   US Librarian

PERSONA non GRATA.

Author: Jorge Edwards

Writer Jorge Edwards (1931) was first diplomatic envoy from Salvador Allende's Chile to Fidel Castro's Cuba. Persona non grata is the memoir of the difficult coexistence between Edwards and the Cuban Revolution which would end with his expulsion from the island. This is the first great critique by a Latin American intellectual of the authoritarianism of a regime which was at the time the object of widespread idealization.

▶ *Alfons Luna*   AFP New York

PERSPECTIVAS CULTURALES de HISPANOAMÉRICA.

Author: Juan Kattan Ibarra

The focus of this book is on crucial Latin American historical events. This book will provide the student with an overall picture of the most important historical events.

▶ *Guillermina Raffo Magnasco*   St. Thomas University

EL PRIMER NUEVA CORÓNICA y BUEN GOBIERNO.

Author: Felipe Guaman Poma de Ayala

NEW

One of the few descriptions of colonial Perú written from the indigenous point of view. The hundreds of detailed drawings by the author illustrate the history of the Inca Empire as well as life during the early colonial period. Written around 1600 the manuscript was rediscovered three hundred years later in the Danish Royal Library in Copenhagen.

▶ *Richard Heyer*   Biblioteca "Jorge Luis Borges"

LAS PRIMERAS REPRESENTACIONES GRÁFICAS del INDIO AMERICANO, 1493-1523.

Author: Ricardo E. Alegría

What place did America occupy in the European imagination of the late 15th century and early 16th century? Professor Ricardo E. Alegria, one of the most prominent figures in Caribbean ethnological studies, follows the clues left to us by witnesses of the first contacts between Europeans and Americans in the Antillean islands. A great bibliographical contribution and an opportunity to take the measure of this beloved Puerto Rican intellectual.

▶ *Pedro Canó*   Instituto Cervantes New York

LA RAZA CÓMICA:
DEL SUJETO EN PUERTO RICO
Author: Rubén Ríos Ávila

A collected literary and cultural criticism by a prize-winning acclaimed writer, La raza cómica is an intelligent and intense model for rethinking culture. Informed by an openly gay sensibility, Ríos Ávila's studies offer a reflection of how the phantasmagoric presence defines the subject. Themes include Palés, the Caribbean as cabaret, and Ramos Otero.

▶ *Nashieli Marcano*   University of Akron

LA REBELIÓN DE LAS MASAS.

Author: José Ortega y Gasset

Of all the philosophical works written in Spanish, The Revolt of the Masses (La rebelión de las masas) is perhaps the one which has been translated more often and has had more intellectual influence on a worldwide scale. This is not mere chance; the book, written in 1926 and published four years later, projects onto a more ambitious global setting the intuitions which its author had sketched in Invertebrate Spain (La España invertebrada), from which society is structured in reciprocal action between the masses and a select minority of citizens. This interaction allows society to evolve, if the minorities are virtuous classes who should guide the general will of the masses toward good actions. In The Revolt of the Masses, Ortega y Gasset anticipated something that at the time few had recognized, namely, the characterization of a new paradigm of the mass-man, a depersonalized being who only thinks of the free expansion and fulfillment of his primary needs and desires and who does not express any gratitude for the historic and social conditions which have made possible his well-being as well as the political normalcy of his existence. A man, who failing to appeal to a higher and virtuous exemplar which he can imitate, becomes easy prey for totalitarian regimes and dictatorships. A paradigm, which, as World War II demonstrated, has survived in our time and perhaps is even more dangerous.

▶ *Bernat Dedéu*   Cadena Ser

RELACIÓN ACERCA DE LAS ANTIGÜEDADES
DE LOS INDIOS.
Authors: Ramón Pané, Fray, and José Juan Arrom, ed.

This Account… was the first document written in the Americas by a European. Ramón Pané, a Catalan friar of the order of St. Jerome, was asked by Columbus to describe the Taino culture he had found in the island of Hispaniola. This is a document of inestimable value for the study of the Caribbean during the time of the encounter between cultures. Lost for centuries until discovered and made public by the researcher José Juan Arrom, in a scholarly edition under his supervision.

▶ *Pedro Canó*   Instituto Cervantes New York

RESPUESTA A SOR FILOTEA.

Author: Sor Juana Inés de la Cruz

In a tone of utter humility, Sister Juana's letter provides one of the best defenses of the right of women to use their intellect. The autobiographical passages that Sister Juana includes make this an enjoyable reading experience, and also contain much information about life in Mexico during the colonial period.

▶ *Paloma Celis Carbajal* UW-Madison

LAS SIETE CIUDADES DE CÍBOLA: TEXTOS Y TESTIMONIOS SOBRE LA EXPEDICIÓN VÁZQUEZ CORONADO.

Author: Pedro de Castañeda Nájera, et al...   NEW

The myth of Cíbola and the Seven Cities of Gold was revived with the stories that Cabeza de Vaca and his companions told upon returning to New Spain and based on Indian accounts of cities filled with great riches. This myth would launch a series of expeditions in search of the mythical cities, the most famous of which was led by Vázquez Coronado. The testimonies of its participants, especially that of Pedro de Castañeda Nájera, show the process that began with a myth and ends in disillusionment. They did not find gold, but they were the first Europeans to admire the Grand Canyon.

▶ *Paloma Graciani* Biblioteca "José Emilio Pacheco"

EL SILENCIO.

Author: Horacio Veerbitsky   NEW

This book investigates the arrests of citizens in Argentina in 1979 and their subsquent internment in concentration camps on the grounds of a religious institution.

▶ *Rafael Pérez Mercado* Biblioteca Pública Raquel Quiñones

TRADUCCIÓN Y TRADUCTOLOGÍA. INTRODUCCIÓN A LA TRADUCTOLOGÍA.

Author: Amparo Hurtado Albir

An excellent and all-encompassing compilation of translation theories with special emphasis placed on modern theories.

▶ *Marko Miletich* Binghamton University (SUNY)

TRADUCCIÓN: LITERATURA Y LITERALIDAD.

Author: Octavio Paz

A lucid exposition of the philosopher's theories which highlights his vision of literary translation as adaptation.

▶ *Marko Miletich* Binghamton University (SUNY)

TRAGICOMEDIA MEXICANA:
LA VIDA EN MÉXICO DE 1940 A 1970.
Author: José Agustín

A very well-documented story that relates, with irony and humor, the great political and economic events of recent years, and also comments on social life, film, the mambo, the 1985 earthquake, the first feminists and Mexican rock.

▷ *Richard Heyer*   Instituto Cervantes New York

LA TRAVESÍA DE ENRIQUE.

Author: Sonia Nazario

The compelling, illuminating account of a young Honduran boy who faces insurmountable odds to reunite with his immigrant mother in the U.S. is told in vivid detail by an award-winning Los Angeles Time journalist.

▷ *Patricia Cuesta*   Los Angeles Public Library

TRAVESÍAS.

Author: Jaime Salinas

Editor Jaime Salinas tells the story of a different exile, of those who left Spain as children because of the Civil War. Son of the poet Pedro Salinas, Jaime Salinas covers thirty years of his life, and especially the formative years: from childhood in Madrid and the Valencian coast, the departure toward France and Algeria when war breaks out, his adaptation to life in North America, his intervention in the World War. The cycle closes when he returns to a Spain which feels strange to him and which he does not know. An interesting portrait of another exile.

▷ *Lluís Agustí*   Instituto Cervantes New York

LAS VENAS ABIERTAS DE AMÉRICA LATINA.

Author: Eduardo Galeano

This is a prominent book indispensable for any Spanish book collection. It presents a historical, political social and economic survey written in an outstanding narrative.

▷ *Alvaro Sanabria*   San Francisco Public Library

VIAJES al ESTRECHO de MAGALLANES.

 Author: Pedro Sarmiento de Gamboa

NEW

A student of mathematics, cosmography, classical languages, and history, a man interested in geography and the customs of the places he visited, this brave sailor Sarmiento de Gamboa filled his account of voyages to the Strait of Magellan with acute observations. Requiered by the Viceroy Toledo to end the depredations of the pirate Drake, the expedition he initiated in 1581 as Captain General of the Strait had the double objective of definitively marking the passage from the Pacific to the Atlantic and of leaving in place a series of permanent settlements.

▶ *Paloma Graciani*   Biblioteca "José Emilio Pacheco"

VIDA MODERNA HISPANA.

 Author: James W. Brown

This book contains a series of interviews to people from different cultures. It is an important learning source to enhance multicultural awareness in our students.

▶ *Guillermina Raffo Magnasco*   St. Thomas University

VISIÓN de ANÁHUAC y otros ENSAYOS.

 Author: Alfonso Reyes

The essays of this collection —with Vision of Anáhuac as a guidepost— offer an example of Alfonso Reyes' extraordinary and superb prose, his rich effects, his colorful palette, his musicality. Reyes is to prose in Spanish what Darío was to poetry: the renovation of the language, the cheerful confirmation of the capacity of the words themselves to go far beyond. The river of images shine with a hypnotic force, with the shine of a real jewel, a pleasure for the senses and intellect of the reader.

▶ *Lluís Agustí*   Instituto Cervantes New York

VIVIR PARA CONTARLA.

Author: Gabriel García Márquez

The complete works of García Márquez are a must but the first volume of his memoirs is another masterpiece. Donna Seaman of the Booklist wrote in her review: "Invaluable in its personal and cultural history, and triumphant in its compassion and artistry, García Márquez's portrait of himself as a young writer is as revelatory and powerful as his fiction."

▶ *Alvaro Sanabria*   San Francisco Public Library

VUDÚ Y MAGIA EN SANTO DOMINGO.

Author: Carlos Esteban Deive

A classic work about the controversial subject of Dominican popular religion and its relationship to Haitian voodoo. Deive describes the rituals, identifies the similarities and differences between both complex ritual traditions, and explains the impressive cosmology which informs Dominican religious practice.

▶ *Pedro Canó*   Instituto Cervantes New York

POETRY / DRAMA

ALTAZOR o el VIAJE en PARACAÍDAS.

Author: Vicente Huidobro

I love Huidobro's character: the ferocity, optimism and impertinence of Non serviam. It is said that Huidobro entered Berlin with the Russians just to steal Hitler's telephone. Altazor is a delectable and ingenious book, full of playful metaphors, almost like a toy train set or a city in miniature.

▶ *Blanca Riestra* Instituto Cervantes Albuquerque

LA AMADA INMÓVIL.

Author: Amado Nervo

NEW

Although many do not recognize Nervo's career as significant, there is no doubt that this volume has transcended academic interest and has become almost compulsory reading in the popular sphere.

▶ *Octavio Núñez* US Librarian

ANIMAL de FONDO.

Author: Juan Ramón Jiménez

"I am an animal of the deep", he writes, and somewhere else, "Desiring and desired God" The later Jiménez is an example of faith in the word, of a vital and heterodox mysticism, of the purity of poetry freed from all limitations.

▶ *Blanca Riestra* Instituto Cervantes Albuquerque

ANTOLOGÍA de la POESÍA BOLIVIANA:
ORDENAR LA DANZA.

Author: Mónica Velásquez Guzmán, ed.

A recent, up-to-date anthology of 20th-century Bolivian poetry. Presented in chronological order, it opens with Ricardo Jaimes Freyre, one of Bolivia's most famous poets, and also includes works by such well-known poets as Franz Tamayo, Gregorio Reynolds, Óscar Cerruto and Eduardo Mitre. The book covers a total of 49 poets in all.

▶ *Eduardo Lago* Instituto Cervantes New York

ANTOLOGÍA DEL GRUPO POÉTICO DE 1927.

 Author: Vicente Gaos, ed.

Although there are critics who cast doubt on the reality of literary generations or groupings, the use of such classifications has enjoyed some success in the presentation of the literary history of a language, and more specifically, of a country. If we refer to the generation of Spanish writers, many of them poets, from the interwar period, the so called Generation of 1927, then undoubtedly that grouping has become an icon, a landmark. Pedro Salinas, Federico García Lorca, Vicente Aleixandre, Jorge Guillén, Gerardo Diego, Rafael Alberti, Emilio Prados, Dámaso Alonso, Luis Cernuda, and Manuel Altolaguirre represent the best of 20th century Spanish poetry.

▶ *Lluís Agustí*   Instituto Cervantes New York

ANTOLOGÍA PERSONAL.

 Author: José Agustín Goytisolo

The Goytisolos, three brothers and writers: José Agustín, poet and translator, Juan and Luis, both storytellers. Jose Agustín Goytisolo, the eldest of the three, belongs the poetic generation of 1950, committed to resistance against Francoism, and like many of the bohemian group, a lover of personal freedom and a great vitalist, sometimes to excess. As Carlos Barral said when referring to them all, "we drank too much." José Agustín Goytisolo's poetry gives expression to that personal option and breaks with all forms of academism, in real and honest verse that makes no concessions, poetry that emanate from the vital impulse itself.

▶ *Lluís Agustí*   Instituto Cervantes New York

ANTOLOGÍA POÉTICA.

 Author: Federico García Lorca

A classic.

▶ *Millie Torrance*   Sacramento Public Library

ANTOLOGÍA POÉTICA.

Author: Josefina Pla

Josefina Pla, Spanish by birth and Paraguayan by choice, left numerous works ranging from poetry and short stories to theater. She is a key figure in understanding 20th-century Paraguayan culture and the way it has developed, especially poetry. Her poems are characterized by their intimate and accessible tone with references to current events, particularly the role and status of women.

▶ *Lluís Agustí*   Instituto Cervantes New York

ANTOLOGÍA POÉTICA.

Author: Antonio Machado.
Indispensable.

▶ *Millie Torrance*   Sacramento Public Library

EL ARPA IMAGINARIA.

Author: Edwin Reyes

Inspired by a great uncle who "sang verses accompanying himself on an imaginary instrument," this collection of poems demonstrates the quality of a poet fully in touch with his people. Edwin Reyes is one of the most original voices in Puerto Rican poetry.

▶ *Sabrina Abreu*   Instituto Cervantes New York

AZUL.

Author: Rubén Darío

No library is complete without a copy of both Cantos de vida y esperanza (Songs of Life and Hope) published in 1905 and this influential collection of poems on its shelves. Rubén Darío was the revered Nicaraguan poet and father of the Spanish-American literary movement known as modernismo – a fusion of the French Parnassian and Symbolist movements. Chilean writer and scholar Ariel Dorfman calls Darío "one of the world's most splendid poets and one of the least known, particularly because of his revolutionary and hybrid style." As a diplomat he traveled extensively, and lived in Chile, Argentina, and Spain. He is extolled for bringing Spanish-language poetry into the modern era, permanently altering its course.

▶ *Claude Potts*   University of California

EL AZUL DE LA TIERRA.

Author: Eugenio Montejo

NEW

This Venezuelan poet is one of the greatest lyricists in the Spanish language, but remains relatively unknown in Spain.

▷ *José María Conget*   Writer

AZUL; ESPAÑA CONTEMPORÁNEA; CANTOS DE VIDA Y ESPERANZA.

Author: Rubén Darío

Darío is probably the most important Nicaraguan poet and his work is beautiful and compact. He had a great influence on the generation which followed.

▷ *Millie Torrance*   Sacramento Public Library

BODAS DE SANGRE.

Author: Federico García Lorca

Based on a true story, Blood Wedding is one of the most powerful, inventive and recognized plays written in modern Spanish literature.

▷ *Alvaro Sanabria*   San Francisco Public Library

EL BURLADOR DE SEVILLA.

Author: Tirso de Molina

Pseudonym of Gabriel Téllez, a Mercederian friar, Tirso de Molina created the first Don Juan drama in world literature. Tirso's hero, Don Juan Tenorio became the inpiration for Moliere, Mozart, Byron and Zorrilla, to cite only the most famous treatments of the theme. Don Juan Tenorio, in Tirso's version, is a titanic character whose reckless defiance of the moral code reaches a level of superhuman courage, which to some extent, redeems his libertinism.

▷ *Eduardo de Lamadrid*   Trans-Lingual Communications Inc.

CAMPOS de CASTILLA.

Author: Antonio Machado

The Sevillano poet Antonio Machado is one of the greatest Spanish poets of all time, while at the same time being the most popular poet in the peninsula. His verse, simple in appearance, comprehensible and familiar, has the power to reach the reader in a sincere and emotional way. He takes as his theme an almost anthropological approach to the country's way of life and its people, exemplified in sad image of the two Spains. A life marked by personal (the death of his wife) and social misfortunes (the Civil War), surfaces in his verse, endowing them with honesty and experience. The Landscape of Castile, his third published work, owes its title to the period when he lived in Soria, where he was a professor.

▶ *Lluís Agustí*   Instituto Cervantes New York

CANCIONERO y ROMANCERO de AUSENCIAS.

Author: Miguel Hernández

In 1930's Spain, Miguel Hernández was a poet of the people and for the people. His determined conduct during the Civil War led to his death in prison in 1942. During the time he was imprisoned, he wrote this beautiful and tragic collection of poems, full of authentic and profound imagery.

▶ *Lluís Agustí*   Instituto Cervantes New York

CANTAR de MÍO CID.

Author: Anonymous

The great medieval Spanish epic, composed by an unknown Castilian juglar (minstrel) in about 1140, but which is preserved in a single copy of 1307 transcribed by one Per Abbat, of whom nothing is known. The reconstructed epic known as the Cantar de Mío Cid (Song of My Cid) is based on other historical materials and is of much later date. The plot of the Poem of the Cid is divided into three parts: the banishment of Rodrigo Díaz (El Cid) by his sovereign; the Cid's victory over the Moors at Valencia, reconciliation with the king, and marriage of his daughters into royalty; and the desertion and cruel treatment of his daughters and trial by combat of the sons-in-law, resulting in the vindication of the Cid's honor. The oldest monument of Castilian literature, the Poem of the Cid is admirable for its realism, its comparative historical fidelity, its fusion of various themes into a unified whole, and as the first and best example of the Spanish "cantar de gesta".

▶ *Eduardo de Lamadrid*   Trans-Lingual Communications Inc.

CANTIGAS DE SANTA MARÍA.

Author: Alfonso X el Sabio

This collection of 420 songs, set to music and gloryfing the miracles performed by the Virgin Mary, was composed by a 13th century king, known as the Wise or the Sage, who was the greatest of all medieval patrons of letters, an encyclopedic scholar and a poet in his own right. Of great power and musicality, the songs were written in Galician, the literary language of the age. Alfonso the Wise also exercised great influence on the development of Castilian prose with works on the law, history and astronomy.

▶ *Eduardo de Lamadrid*   Trans-Lingual Communications Inc.

CANTO GENERAL.

Author: Pablo Neruda
                                        NEW

This is possibly the most important volume of Hispanic American poetry of the 20th century. This offering by the Chilean Nobel Prize winner is required reading and included in the canon of Western civilization.

▶ *Octavio Núñez*   US Librarian

CANTOS DE VIDA Y ESPERANZA.

Author: Rubén Darío

This work by the great Nicaraguan poet sets forth exotic themes as well as themes about the poet's "search for his own self". Rubén Darío is conidered by many critics to be one of the most influential modernist poets from Latin America. These poems touch upon exotic themes and the poet's quest for spiritual fulfilment.

▶ *Ismael Alicea*   The New York Public Library

LA CASA DE BERNARDA ALBA.

Author: Federico García Lorca

Considered to be Lorca's highest dramatic achievement, besides being one of the most well-known and dramatized works of the Spanish theater. The subtitle of the play is Drama of women in the villages of Spain. It focuses on the life of an Andalusian family in which the protagonist exercises a cruel tyranny over her five daughters. This drama explores the themes of repression, passion and nonconformity in a rural feminine world. It is worth noting the apparent simplicity of the work counterpoised against its enormous thematic complexity.

▶ *Paloma Celis Carbajal*   UW-Madison

EL CASTILLO INTERIOR o las MORADAS.

Author: Santa Teresa de Jesús

Santa Teresa de Jesús represents the humanization of mysticism. In her greatest mystical work, she narrates the ascent of her soul through the seven chambers of the mystic castle to complete union with God. Her basic message is the extinction of self and submergence into the Divine Essence. Yet her style is conversational and full of native humor and pungency. Her many achievements are related in her Libro de las fundaciones and her inner life is revealed in her introspective autobiography, Libro de su vida.

▶ *Eduardo de Lamadrid*   Trans-Lingual Communications Inc.

CICLO MÁGICO de las ESTACIONES.

Author: Francisco Alarcón
NEW

Alarcón has written a series of bilingual poems for each season. He dips into nostalgia from his childhood to craft these poems set in Los Angeles, California.

▶ *Sherry Lord*   Claremont Inmersion in Arlington

CIEN SONETOS de AMOR.

Author: Pablo Neruda

This work is very popular as well as being beautiful.

▶ *Millie Torrance*   Sacramento Public Library

CUADERNO de NUEVA YORK.

Author: José Hierro
NEW

José Hierro is considered to be one of the great contemporary poets working in the Spanish language. New York Notebook, comprised of 32 poems and heralded by the critics as a major work of contemporary poetry, is one of his most emblematic books and perfectly summarizes the themes which have always interested him. His poetry expresses a deep concern for social and human issues, the passage of time, and memory. José Hierro was awarded the Cervantes Prize for Letters in 1998.

▶ *Salvador Vergara*   Instituto Cervantes Chicago

EL DECIR y el VÉRTIGO:
PANORAMA DE LA POESÍA HISPANOAMERICANA RECIENTE (1963-1979).

Authors: Rocío Cerón, Julián Herbert, and León Plascencia Ñol.

The anthologists, active poets with important works of their own and experienced editors, have taken on the arduous task of offering an overview of Hispanic-American poetry produced by authors born between 1965 and 1979. Taking into account the difficulty of achieving such an objective, El decir y el vértigo, beyond presenting a comprehensive Hispanic-American vision, manages to place within the reader's purview several young voices which, either by radical experimentation or by entries more closely tied to tradition, constitute the new poetic trailblazers of the region. In this sense, the selection is a useful tool in terms of familiarizing the reader with the works of the Argentine Fabián Casas, the Colombians Felipe García Quintero and Pascual Gaviria, the Chileans Germán Carrasco and Javier Bello, the Peruvian Paul Guillén, the Cuban Damaris Calderón and the Mexicans Luis Vicente de Aguinaga, Ernesto Lumbreras and Eduardo Padilla, among others. Likewise, the anthology represents a very important attempt to create links and establish a dialogue among the poets of the Hispanic-American world.

▶ *Gaspar Orozco*   Mexican Poet and Diplomat

DEL LADO del AMOR.

Author: Juan Antonio González Iglesias   **NEW**

Juan Antonio González Iglesias is one of the most distinctive voices in Spanish contemporary poetry. His poems are deeply connected with the classical tradition and rooted in topics such as love and beauty, shedding new light on those topics from a contemporary gaze.

▶ *Jesús Alonso Regalado*   University of Albany

DIARIO de ARGÓNIDA.

Author: José Manuel Caballero Bonald

"The more I age the more life I have left", concludes one of the poems of Argolis Diary (Diario de Argónida). Published when the Andalusian poet José Manuel Cabellero Bonald was over 70, this beautiful collection of crepuscular poems, full of experienced life, is a paean to fellow travelers "with little remorse and no abnegation," to the geographic space the poet inhabits and where he declares himself. In short, this is a beautiful and happy elegy, the retelling and celebration of an existence —with errors no doubt— lived to the fullest.

▶ *Lluís Agustí*   Instituto Cervantes New York

EL LIBRO DEL FRÍO.

Author: Antonio Gamoneda

Formed by "blocks of language" assembled with an exact balance of musicality and sense, the prose poems of this book enter unnamed territories where lightning illumines the earth for a second and eroticism reveals the body for a dark instant. At journey's end, since these poems are in many senses a voyage, we can say with the poet "now there is only light inside my eyes." With El libro del frío, Antonio Gamoneda (Oviedo, 1931) has made a solid contribution to poetry in Spanish written on both sides of the Atlantic.

▶ *Gaspar Orozco*   Mexican Poet and Diplomat

EN QUÉ CREEN LOS QUE NO CREEN.

Author: Umberto Eco

NEW

Reflections about the basis of ethics and other values questioned by contemporary man.

▶ *Rafael Pérez Mercado*   Biblioteca Pública Raquel Quiñones

FUENTEOVEJUNA.

Author: Lope de Vega

Spain's most prolific and greatest dramatist, Lope is said to have written more than 400 plays, many of which were comedies of the "capa y espada" (cloak and dagger) variety. Fuenteovejuna is a historical comedy, based on an actual happening, set against a background of historical fact, and peopled with peasants, royalty and a villanous nobleman. It is startling today for its use of a collective protagonist, the town of Fuenteovejuna, and its overt populism.

▶ *Eduardo de Lamadrid*   Trans-Lingual Communications Inc.

INVENTARIO I, II AND III.

Author: Mario Benedetti

NEW

Collection of poems of one of the most prominent Latin American writers: the Uruguayan journalist, novelist, and poet Mario Benedetti. Each volume covers different stages of the author's works from 1950 to 2001.

▶ *Norma Medina Ortiz*   Seminole County Public Library System

LA CAJA NEGRA.

Author: Juan Carlos Quintero

This rich and hermetic book of poems contains a collection of verses that brings together multiple tones and cultural traditions, in a very Caribbean style.

▷ *Nashieli Marcano*   University of Akron

LA CELESTINA.

Author: Fernando de Rojas

This dramatized novel is considered by critics second only to Don Quixote in intrinsic greatness and literary influence. The plot deals with the love of Calisto for Melibea, whose initial indifference promtos him to engage the services of a go-between, who deviously persuades the girl to respond to her lover's suit. It ends tragically with the death of both lovers. The greatness of the novel lies in its realistic delineation of character. The crone, Celestina, a panderess of titanic cunning, is depicted as evil incarnate. Other characters such as the picaresque servants, the prostitutes, the braggart soldiers etc. present a vivid pictue of life among the common people of early 16th century Spain. Even Calisto, with his flowery diction and his abject adoration, is a faithful portrayal of the Petrarcan lover of the day.

▷ *Eduardo de Lamadrid*   Trans-Lingual Communications Inc.

LA VIDA es SUEÑO.

Author: Pedro Calderón de la Barca.

Why a 17th century text? Because life is a dream and dreams are dreams as well. Calderón knew it then and it is still true today.

▷ *Adan Griego*   Stanford University Libraries

LAS LENGUAS de DIAMANTE.

Author: Juana de Ibarbourou

An exponent of the best female Latin American poetry of all time, this extraordinary poet offers a sample of her best poetry in this volume.

▷ *Octavio Núñez*   US Librarian

LIBRO DE BUEN AMOR.

Authors: Juan Ruiz Archipreste de Hita

The greatest of all Spanish "mester de clerecía" works and a comic masterpiece. The "buen amor" of the title refers to spiritual love as contrasted with "amor loco", carnal love. Although nominally favoring the former, the first-person narrator makes a concession to human frailty by dwelling at length on the former. Juan Ruiz goes far beyond the theme of love, introducing a satire of medieval life and manners. Unforgettable characters are Trotaconventos, an old hag who is the hero's panderess and the prototype for all future go-betweens in Spanish literature, and Don Furón, the hero's rascally servant. Memorable also is the "parade of sausages" which anticipates Rabelais. This is a work by a good humored, jovial human being, yet who is also profoundly religious, charitable and tolerant. Quintessentially Spanish in his love of proverbs, little things and the anecdotal, he grounds his dreams and visions in real life.

▶ *Eduardo de Lamadrid*   Trans-Lingual Communications Inc.

LUCES DE BOHEMIA.

Author: Ramón María del Valle Inclán

Valle-Inclán creates the theater of the grotesque, that is, the deformed and bizarre vision of reality, which according to the author himself was the best means of expressing the tragicomic Spanish reality of the early 20th century. The main character, a miserable poet called Max Estrella, lives out a bohemian night in Madrid and comes across a heterogeneous gallery of sad, tragic, and failed characters.

▶ *Lluís Agustí*   Instituto Cervantes New York

NO AMANECE EL CANTOR.

Author: José Angel Valente

A painful and ascetic work, yet full of beauty, from one of the most interesting poets end of the 20th century, who always followed his own instincts. It disdains expressive excess; the poetic verb is handled with a religious, almost austere, reverence.

▶ *Blanca Riestra*   Instituto Cervantes Albuquerque

NOTICIAS del EXTRANJERO.

 Author: Pedro Lastra

The first edition of News from Abroad was published a little over 25 years ago. During that period, this slim volume of poems has been reissued in numerous editions in various countries of the hemisphere. At the same time, slowly and patiently, new poems have been incorporated to its pages. The Chilean poet and academic Pedro Lastra (1932) locates the exact point between the immediate present and memory; from there, he names with absolute precision the beings and the absences which inhabit the days. For years a closely kept secret, News from Abroad is today, and justifiably so, a classic of Hispanic-American literature.

▶ *Gaspar Orozco*   Mexican Poet and Diplomat

NUEVE NOVÍSIMOS POETAS ESPAÑOLES.

 Author: J.M. Castellet, selec.

Critic and editor Josep Maria Castellet's selection in 1970 of the most innovative Spanish poets of the time has become a canonical work and created the idea of a group, if not united by generation or aesthetic, do share attitudes relative to language, poetic form and poetry itself. Included were poets Manuel Vázquez Montalbán, Antonio Martínez Sarrión, José María Alvarez, Félix de Azúa, Pere Gimferrer, Vicente Molina-Foix, Guillermo Carnero, Ana María Moix, and Leopoldo María Panero.

▶ *Lluís Agustí*   Instituto Cervantes New York

OBRA POÉTICA COMPLETA.

 Author: Jorge Carrera Andrade

This book gathers together the complete poetry of Jorge Carrera Andrade, considered—and rightly so—to be the best Ecuadorean poet of the 20th century. Carrera Andrade uses short forms that are largely free of Baroque mannerisms and close to the poetry of Asia, with a marvelous capacity for depicting landscape and impressions through visual metaphor. "Purify the world of shadowy thoughts—this is the essence. Let the eye ready its ship for a new discovery."

▶ *Lluís Agustí*   Instituto Cervantes New York

Obra poética.

Author: Jorge Luis Borges

Since the beginning, Jorge Luis Borges' poetical work seems to have been eclipsed by the fame garnered by his stories, yet the literary quality and worth of his poems is beyond dispute. As ingenious as his prose, and possessing the rhythms and melodies only known to a blind man, who instead of writing, recreates from memory, these poems have all the beauty and erudition of the stories, along with a musicality conducive to oral recitation.

▶ *Lluís Agustí*   Instituto Cervantes New York

Obra poética.

Author: Iñigo López de Mendoza Santillana, Marqués de

This early Renaissance poet, critic, soldier and statesman introduced the sonnet form to Spanish literature. Yet his best lyrics are inspired by folk themes and forms derived from Galician poetry (canciones, decires, serranillas and villancicos). Santillana is distinguished for his delicate grace and sentiment expressed in simple form.

▶ *Eduardo de Lamadrid*   Trans-Lingual Communications Inc.

Obras completas:
Poesía completa y prosa selecta.
Author: Alejandra Pizarnik

The brief life—cut short by her own hand—of this extraordinary Argentine poet has made her complete works, recommended here, fit into one volume. Despite their often tormented origin, her poems are clear, transparent, polished. "She who died because of her blue dress is singing. Imbued with death, she sings to the sun of her intoxication."

▶ *Lluís Agustí*   Instituto Cervantes New York

Obras escogidas.

Author: San Juan de la Cruz

San Juan de la Cruz is the greatest of all the mystic poets and one of the greatest lyric poets the world has known. The humblest of men, he does not seek to describe the mystical experience itself. His rapturous spiritual joy overflows spontaneously in poetic lyricism, so that his verse does not directly state, but rather, suggests and stimulates the imagination. The bucolic simplicity of his verses conceals untold depths of significance. Works such La subida del Monte Carmelo, Noche oscura del alma, Llama de amor viva, and Cántico espiritual are masterpieces not only of Spanish, but also of world literature.

▶ *Eduardo de Lamadrid*   Trans-Lingual Communications Inc.

PALABRA sobre PALABRA:
OBRA COMPLETA (1956-2001).
Author: Angel González

Angel González is a poet of profound social and human thinking and a skeptic from experience, but who, in spite of all, wants to keep writing. Perplexed and preoccupied by the world and the people who inhabit it in the absence of God, the poet has created beautiful texts which question reason and the relationship with the other, the "you", the self, time and death.

▶ *Lluís Agustí*　　　　　　　　　　　Instituto Cervantes New York

PIC-NIC. EL TRICICLO. EL LABERINTO.

Author: Fernando Arrabal

Cara Randall suggested this book saying Arrabal writes absurd drama (a bit like Ionesco). He's studied in literature classes. This book has 3 of his best in one volume.

▶ *Millie Torrance*　　　　　　　　　　Sacramento Public Library

PIEDRA de SOL.

NEW

Author: Octavio Paz

Although this Nobel Prize winner is renown for the clarity and precision of his poetry, this volume undoubtedly stands out, among all the others, for its force and distinctive style.

▶ *Octavio Núñez*　　　　　　　　　　　US Librarian

LA PIEL de TORO.

Author: Salvador Espriu

Espriu's most important collection of poems and the one which establishes most clearly his voice of denunciation and admonition against Francoism.

▶ *Jaume Martí Olivella*　　　　　　　　University of New Hampshire

POEMAS CLANDESTINOS.

Author: Roque Dalton

By one of the most recognized poets of El Salvador, in this collection of poems, the author in the voice of five imaginary poets conveys the political insight of his country.

▶ *Alvaro Sanabria*　　　　　　　　　San Francisco Public Library

POEMAS PÓSTUMOS.

Author: Jaime Gil de Biedma

Jaime Gil de Biedma is one of the most influential poetic voices of the so-called Generation of 1950, also known as the Barcelona School. Gil de Biedma's poetry is autobiographical, notably realist in nature, and occasionally delves into social criticism. Posthumous collections, Persons of the Verb (Las personas del verbo) and To Return (Volver) are the beginning, and the best example, of the mode known as Poetry of Experience. Poetry of Experience and Poetry of Knowledge are the two fundamental currents of Spanish poetry at the end of the 20th century.

▶ *Lluís Agustí*   Instituto Cervantes New York

POESÍA VARIA.

Author: Francisco de Quevedo

Although better known for his picaresque novels, Quevedo is nonetheless one of Spain's greatest poets. By temperament sarcastic, his pungent wit and mordant satire are evident in his verse, although he also wrote great metaphysical and love poems. His poems range from brief epigrams to long heroic poems, from the off-color to the deeply religious. He was an obdurate opponent of Culteranismo and Góngora, whom he satirized mercilessly. As an example of his power to ridicule, read the sonnet "A una nariz" (To a Nose) and as example of metaphysical love read the sonnet "Amor constante más alla de la muerte" (Constant Love Beyond Death), hailed by Dámaso Alonso as the greatest sonnet in Spanish literature.

▶ *Eduardo de Lamadrid*   Trans-Lingual Communications Inc.

POESÍA.

Author: Jorge Manrique

"Let from its dream the soul awaken, and reason mark with open eyes, the scene unfolding, How lightly life is taken, How cometh Death in stealthy guise, at last beholding; What swiftness hath the flight of pleasure that, once attained, seems nothing more than respite cold." In 1476, upon his father's death, soldier and poet Jorge Manrique wrote the Coplas, some of the most beatufiul verses ever written in Spanish, in which the idea and image of the passage of time, memory, the sadness which provokes happiness in remembrance will find a resolution diffuclt to surpass.

▶ *Lluís Agustí*   Instituto Cervantes New York

POESÍA.

Author: Ausiàs March

The most important poet of medieval Catalan literature, he introduced Renaissance and Petrarchan forms and themes to the literatures of the Iberian peninsula.

▷ *Jaume Martí Olivella* University of New Hampshire

POESÍA.

Author: Fray Luis de León

Like Garcilaso, Fray Luis de León's enduring fame rests on a handful of lyric poems, all of impeccable style and beauty. A master of the lira form, which he used in some of his best poems, "Vida retirada," "A Francisco Salinas," "Noche serena", etc., which are monuments to precision, technical perfection and depth of meaning. Idea and form, humanism and religion, appreciation of beaty and austerity of moral conception in him are completely blended. Hence the widely accepted view of Fray Luis as the incarnation of maximum harmony of the late Spanish Renaissance.

▷ *Eduardo de Lamadrid* Trans-Lingual Communications Inc.

POESÍAS CASTELLANAS COMPLETAS.

Author: Garcilaso de la Vega

"Corrientes aguas puras, cristalinas..." Thus flows Garcilaso's verse: pure, limpid, crystal clear. A consummate artist, his poems are models of form and beauty. This conscientious regard for perfection may account for his limited output: 38 sonnets, 5 songs, 3 eclogues, 2 elegies, one epistle and 8 coplas. He introduced Italian hendecasyllable verse and the metrical form known as the lira to Spanish verse. Yet this greatest of Spanish Renaissance poets is no mere formalist, and expresses the authentic, sincere sentiment of love with the melancholy and frustrated Platonism of the age.

▷ *Eduardo de Lamadrid* Trans-Lingual Communications Inc.

POESÍAS LÍRICAS.

Author: Lope de Vega

Lope is also one of Spain's greatest lyrical poets, and wrote in all the forms of verse known in his day. With an extraordinary command of language and lyrical facility, he treated a universal array of themes, classical and contemporary, sacred and profane. Although at odds with Góngora, he did make some concessions to the prevaling vogue of Conceptismo.

▷ *Eduardo de Lamadrid* Trans-Lingual Communications Inc.

POESÍAS.

Author: Luis de Góngora

The most important poetic texts of the Spanish Baroque period, of profound transcendence in the 17th century and renewed influence in the 20th century.

▶ *Isaías Lerner*   CUNY

POETA EN NUEVA YORK.

Author: Federico García Lorca

This is probably one of the best book of poems written about New York City. Just read "Oda a Walt Whitman", and I think you'll agree.

▶ *Ismael Alicea*   The New York Public Library

PROSAS PROFANAS.

Author: Rubén Darío

Because it is, in the words of José Olivio Jiménez, "the insurmountable summit of all Modernist Aestheticism", and, as such, the signpost for all subsequent poetry in Spanish.

▶ *Isaías Lerner*   CUNY

¿QUÉ SE AMA CUANDO SE AMA?.

Author: Gonzalo Rojas   **NEW**

Qué se ama cuando se ama? is the title of an extraordinary collection of erotic poems by this important Chilean poet, a member of the Generation of 1938. His work is framed within the continuing tradition of the literary Latin American vanguard of the 20th century. Wide recognized in Hispanic America, he has been awarded, among others, the Queen Sofia Prize for Iberian-American Poetry (1992), the National Literature Prize of Chile (1994), and the Cervantes Prize (2003), and is generally considered to be one of Chile's greatest poet.

▶ *Marcelo Ayala*   Instituto Cervantes Chicago

RENAISSANCE AND BAROQUE POETRY OF SPAIN.

Author: Elias L. Rivers

These are classical poems from the Renaissance and the Baroque. Used by FAU, this volume may be very helpful to American students since it is simultaneously translated into English.

▶ *Guillermina Raffo Magnasco*   St. Thomas University

RESIDUOS de los TIEMPOS.

Author: Enrique Laguerre

On his first book of poems—published at the age of 94—Laguerre, one of the most renowned Puerto Rican authors of the 20th century, gives his readers his most intimate and lyric voice and opens them to his internal world of infancy, love, time, nation and nature.

▷ *Nashieli Marcano*   University of Akron

RIMAS y LEYENDAS.

Author: Gustavo Adolfo Bécquer

Written by the most outstanding figure of Spanish Romanticism, the texts included in this volume offer the best example of Romantic poetry and poetic prose, and contain practically every characteristic of the Romantic period.

▷ *Octavio Núñez*   US Librarian

ROMANCERO GITANO.

Author: Federico García Lorca

García Lorca's poetry is universal. These beautiful poems about life, death and gypsy superstitions are breathtaking.

▷ *Ismael Alicea*   The New York Public Library

SONETOS.

Author: Luis de Góngora

The greatest and most complex poet of the late Golden Age, Góngora is synonomous with Culteranismo, a poetic school which relates mythological themes brimming with esoteric allusions and violent conceits (Conceptismo). Yet his sonnets, which are dense in imagery and metaphor, are distinguished by grace, charm, wit and vitality, and are much more accesible to modern readers than the lexically, syntactically and figuratively complex Polifemo y Galatea and the Soledades.

▷ *Eduardo de Lamadrid*   Trans-Lingual Communications Inc.

SÓNGORO COSONGO.

 Author: Nicolás Guillén

The great Cuban poet Nicolás Guillén wrote that the following verses were born not composed: "In this land, mulata, of Africans and Spaniards, St. Barbara on one side and Changó on the other." And it's true, Nicolás Guillén's poetry is a new poetry, a mestizo poetry, authentically musical, where the melody might be Spanish, but the rhythm is unmistakably African, a poetry which seems destined for song and for the dance, and which is based on the historical vindication of a color, the color black. Sóngoro cosongo is a book of poems which should be read aloud.

▶ *Lluís Agustí*   Instituto Cervantes New York

TALA.

Author: Gabriela Mistral

Chilean poet Gabriela Mistral was the first Spanish American writer to win the Nobel Prize in Literature. But that is not the reason we are suggesting her work in this bibliography. Tala is an excellent book, genuine and passionate. Published in 1938, it was dedicated to the Basque children who suffered the hardships of the Spanish Civil War and of exile.

▶ *Lluís Agustí*   Instituto Cervantes New York

TEATRO ESPAÑOL DE VANGUARDIA.

Author: Agustín Muñoz-Alonso López, ed.

Las obras dramáticas de Federecio García Lorca -algunas de ellas incluidas también en esta selección- son sin duda las más divulgadas y populares del teatro de experimentación español del primer tercio del siglo XX. Junto a estas, se presentan las de otros autores desconocidas por el gran público pero sin duda con un alto valor teatral y literario: Corpus Barga, Antonio Espina, José Bergamín, Max Aub, José Bello y Luis Buñuel, Claudio de la Torre, Rafael Alberti, o Agustín Espinosa.

▶ *Lluís Agustí*   Instituto Cervantes New York

TESOROS DE LA POESÍA EN LA LENGUA CASTELLANA.

Author: Regino García Badell

This book contains a splendid selection of Spanish and Latin American poetry. It provides a regular index, name index and first line verses index. It also includes a preface by the famous Spanish poet Rafael Alberti.

▶ *Alvaro Sanabria*   San Francisco Public Library

TRILCE.

Author: César Vallejo

This collection of poems both a bit sad and sweet is the companion piece to a previous volume and is marked by a boldness and profundity that will take away the reader's breath. Vallejo parts company with Surrealism to create his own expressive credo which only consists in surrendering to his own boundless and dark voice.

▶ *Blanca Riestra*   Instituto Cervantes Albuquerque

TUNTÚN DE PASA Y GRIFERÍA.

Author: Luis Palés Matos

This work represents classic Negro poetry at its best. Luis Palés Matos from Puerto Rico and Nicolás Guillén from Cuba are considered to be the best exponents of the Afro-Antillean genre. This work represents classic Afro-Antillean poetry at its best.

▶ *Ismael Alicea*   The New York Public Library

VEINTE POEMAS DE AMOR Y UNA CANCIÓN DESESPERADA.

Author: Pablo Neruda

The poems contained in this small volume by this Nobel Prize winner are still required reading and always included in anthologies compiling the best love poetry in the Spanish language.

▶ *Octavio Núñez*   US Librarian

VERSIÓN CELESTE.

Author: Juan Larrea.

A very beautiful yet anomalous book, which owes something to both Ultraism and Creationism, and more to Surrealism, written in almost all its entirety in French by a poet who sought the limits of language in his own reticence. It contains two of my favorite poems of all time, "Quarry (Flesh, my dear dynamite)" and "Reason (Succession of sounds moving to the gleam)", translated at one time by a very young Gerardo Diego.

▶ *Blanca Riestra*   Instituto Cervantes Albuquerque

VERSOS LIBRES.

Author: José Martí

NEW

A classic of 19th century poetry, included in practically every literature program in schools in Hispanic America and in Spanish programs in the United States.

▶ *Octavio Núñez*   US Librarian

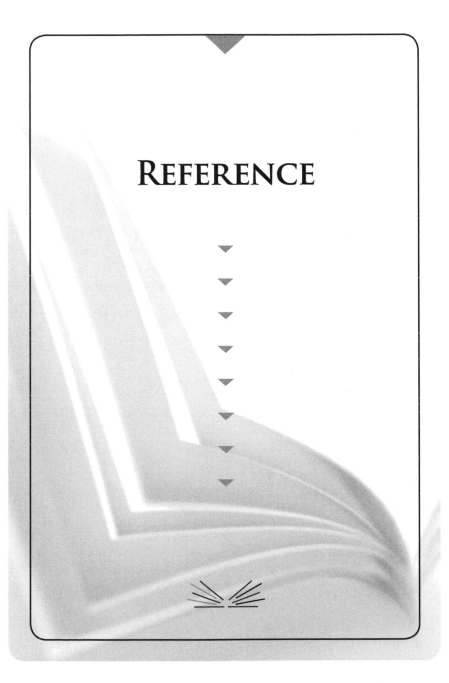

REFERENCE

100 CARTAS PERSONALES.

Author: Juan Sebastián González

NEW

This very useful collection of letter templates offers an easy lesson in effective communication and is appropriate especially to public library users. Letters are conveniently divided into sections such as invitations, thank you, employment and other practicalities.

> *Mónica Chapa Domercq*   Oceanside Public Library

ANTOLOGÍA CRÍTICA DEL CINE ESPAÑOL:

1906-1995.
Author: Julio Pérez Perucha, ed.

From close to 6,000 titles which comprise the history of Spanish film to date, a group of academic and film researchers selected 305 films considered key to the history of our cinematographic tradition and provided an interesting critical study of each selection. This work was sponsored by the Spanish Association of Film Historians. Indispensable for both libraries and film buffs.

> *Lluís Agustí*   Instituto Cervantes New York

CINE ARGENTINO.

Author: Claudio España, ed.

This work can be currently divided into three others: Argentine Film under Democracy: 1983-1993; Argentine Film: Industry and Classicism, 1933-1956; and Argentine Film: Modernity and the Avant-Garde, 1957-1983. Sponsored by the National Fund for the Arts and written by the most prominent historians of Argentine film, the work is organized by themes and plots, and the films are considered in the context of Argentine history. An excellent analytical work, indispensable for both libraries and film buffs.

> *Lluís Agustí*   Instituto Cervantes New York

CINE DOCUMENTAL en AMÉRICA LATINA.

Author: Paulo Antonio Paranaguá

This resource contains extensive (6-20 page) biographies of fifteen Latin American documentary film makers, as well as a chronological list of major films in this genre from 1921 to 2002. Also included is a selection of essays on the subject and a thirty-page bibliography of related sources.

> *Teresa Chapa*   University of North Carolina at Chapel Hill

DICCIONARIO CRÍTICO ETIMOLÓGICO
CASTELLANO e HISPÁNICO.
Author: Joan Corominas

This is the etymological dictionary par excellence of the Spanish language. In its six volumes, the reader will be able to find not only the origin of a given word, but also documented examples of how the word was originally used and its subsequent evolution.

▶ *Paloma Celis Carbajal*   UW-Madison

DICCIONARIO de AUTORES
LATINOAMERICANOS.
Author: César Aira

César Aira is a well-known Argentine novelist, translator, dramatist and essayist. Two facts about this work are worth reporting: Aira specifically dedicates himself to the search for forgotten, unknown authors, and no author appearing after the 1990's is included.

▶ *Lluís Agustí*   Instituto Cervantes New York

DICCIONARIO de AUTORES
PUERTORRIQUEÑOS CONTEMPORÁNEOS.
Author: Victor F. Torres

NEW

A great reference work with brief, yet informative entries on the current literature of Puerto Rico. Can serve users in need of suggested readings as well as a tool for collection development.

▶ *Adan Griego*   Stanford University

DICCIONARIO de DUDAS y DIFICULTADES
de la LENGUA ESPAÑOLA.
Author: Manuel Seco

As its title indicates, a dictionary of usage problems has the objective of helping the speaker resolve quandaries relative to both speech and writing in those aspects of the language where there is uncertainty concerning forms and usage. Language scholar Manuel Seco is a figure of renown in the field of lexicography and this dictionary is a classic which has undergone numerous editions in response to new challenges presented by a linguistic reality in constant evolution.

▶ *Lluís Agustí*   Instituto Cervantes New York

DICCIONARIO DE ESCRITORES EN LENGUA CASTELLANA: QUIÉN ES QUIÉN HOY EN LAS LETRAS ESPAÑOLAS.
Author: Twiggy Hirota, ed.

An updated edition of Balay BE1458/Walford7 3:#8298, the 1988 edition having slipped through the cracks. Now limited to writers in Castilian. Entries indicate place and year of birth, present position with an occasional address, published works, anthologies, and prizes. No index.

▶ *Jeffry Larson*   Yale University Library

 ## DICCIONARIO DE LA LENGUA ESPAÑOLA.
Author: Real Academia Española

The Dictionary of the Royal Spanish Academy, commonly known by its Spanish acronym DRAE, is undoubtedly the official dictionary of the Spanish language, and is accepted as such by a great majority of Spanish speakers.

▶ *Paloma Celis Carbajal*   UW-Madison

 ## DICCIONARIO DE LA LITERATURA ESPAÑOLA E HISPANOAMERICANA.
Author: Ricardo Gullón, dir.

An excellent dictionary of authors, themes and movements of Spanish and Hispanic-American literatures of all times. A key reference work due to its informational value and quality. The entries are signed and include a brief bibliography at the end.

▶ *Lluís Agustí*   Lluís Agustí

 ## DICCIONARIO DE LA MÚSICA ESPAÑOLA E HISPANOAMERICANA.
Authors: Emilio Casares Rodicio, dir. y coord. gral, José López-Calo, dir., and Ismael Fernández de la Cuesta, dir.

A comprehensive reference work about music in Spain and Hispanic-American countries. Contains more than 24,000 entries which cover the history, characteristics, relationships, resources and protagonists of Spanish and Hispanic-American musical culture. Includes biographies of composers, singers, dancer, musicologists, teachers, librettists, instrument makers, music critics and promoters, set designers, editors and printers, writers, choreographers, philosophers, scientists and businessmen connected to the music world. This work was sponsored by General Association of Authors and Editors (SGAE) and by the National Institute of Theatrical Arts and Music (INAEM), a dependency of Spain's Ministry of Education, Culture and Sports.

▶ *Lluís Agustí*   Instituto Cervantes New York

DICCIONARIO DEL CINE ESPAÑOL.

Author: José Luis Borau, ed.

This dictionary was sponsored and endorsed by the Academy of Cinematographic Arts and Sciences of Spain. It contains approximately 1,400 entries arranged alphabetically with information about directors, actors, producers, screen writers, film festivals, production houses, etc. It includes a terminal index for more than 5,000 film titles with references to the entry or entries for the articles in which they are cited.

▶ *Lluís Agustí*   Instituto Cervantes New York

DICCIONARIO DEL QUIJOTE:
LA OBRA PARA ENTENDER UNO DE LOS LIBROS ESENCIALES DE LA CULTURA UNIVERSAL.
Author: César Vidal

After a 131-page introduction that sets the novel in its context, this semi-scholarly dictionary covers the terms, characters, and themes in Cervantes' masterpiece. Omits mention of Howard Mancing's Cervantes encyclopedia (see Choice, Sept. 2004). Includes cross references and a 68-page bibliography; no index.

▶ *Jeffry Larson*   Yale University Library

DICCIONARIO DEL USO DEL ESPAÑOL.

Author: María Moliner

Extraordinary reference work for readers interested in more than just one simple definition of a word. In the words of its author, this work was conceived as a guide to Spanish usage for both native speakers and those students who have reached that point in their knowledge where a dictionary in the language being learned should be substituted for the bilingual dictionary. And so, firstly, it provides the user with all the resources available in the language needed to name a thing, to express an idea with maximum precision, or to realize verbally any expressive act. And secondly, it resolves the user's doubts about the legitimacy or illegitimacy of an expression, about the correct way to resolve a certain construction, and so on.

▶ *Paloma Celis Carbajal*   UW-Madison

DICCIONARIO DEL VERBO ESPAÑOL,
HISPANOAMERICANO Y DIALECTAL.
Author: Jaime Suances Torres

Conjugations, etymologies, definitions and specific usages of countries and regions. Regular, semi-regular, and irregular conjugations. A must have reference book.

▶ *Lluís Agustí*   Instituto Cervantes New York

DICCIONARIO FRASEOLÓGICO DOCUMENTADO
DEL ESPAÑOL ACTUAL: LOCUCIONES Y MODISMOS.
Author: Manuel Seco

A scholarly dictionary of Spanish phrases and locutions based on the author's general Diccionario del espanõl actual (1999), noted in our Fall 2000 issue. Entries indicate variants, grammatical categories, level and area of usage, as well as sourced illustrative citations. Includes a 22-page bibliography of cited texts.

▶ *Jeffry Larson*   Yale University Library

DICCIONARIO IDEOLÓGICO
DE LA LENGUA ESPAÑOLA.
Author: Julio Casares

Julio Casares' lexicographical work is a great aid for writing clearly and richly, and for finding the exact words which sometimes escape us. This dictionary includes, besides the alphabetic entries common to any dictionary, and ideological classification of words, to proceed, as the author says, "from the idea to the word; from the word to the idea". Words are presented organized by analogy, by semantic relationships and by families of ideas. Equally useful for writers, translators or person who wish to express themselves with precision, relevance and clarity.

▶ *Lluís Agustí*   Instituto Cervantes New York

DICCIONARIO PANHISPÁNICO DE DUDAS.

Author: Real Academia Española

Twenty-two academies of the Spanish language collaborated for five years in the making of this dictionary, a tool whose objective is to resolve questions related to Spanish usage across the entire community of Spanish speakers.

▶ *Paloma Celis Carbajal*   UW-Madison

ENCICLOPEDIA DE LA NOVELA ESPAÑOLA.

Author: Rafael del Moral

In the manner of Porto Bompiani historic literary dictionary, Rafael del Moral includes a selection of more than 700 Spanish novels, each of which is given a brief reference about the subject and intention of the author, a summary of the plot, a brief textual analysis of the novel's style and characters, a critic's appreciation and its connection to other works. A complementary bibliography follows each entry. The objective of the work is not critical appraisal, but rather to provide orientation to professors and students, to help readers decide on new reading, or as a mnemonic aid to remember specifics about readings. And of course, it can't be avoided, it also helps students who have not read the book with their task.

▶   *Lluís Agustí*   Instituto Cervantes New York

ENCICLOPEDIA HISPÁNICA.

The Enciclopedia Hispánica is the one the most authoritative, up-to-date, and comprehensive encyclopedia published in Spanish.

▶   *Alvaro Sanabria*   San Francisco Public Library

ENCYCLOPEDIA LATINA:
HISTORY, CULTURE AND SOCIETY IN THE UNITED STATES.

Author: Ilan Stavans, editor in chief, and Harold Augenbraum, associate editor.

In spite of it alphabetical order, this reference work is more precisely a thematic encyclopedia, with emphasis on aspects of the culture, society, language and art of Latinos in the United States. The work is not exempt from the controversy often provoked by the work of Ilan Stavans, see, for example, the entry for Spanglish. Each entry is followed by cross-references and a complementary bibliography.

▶   *Lluís Agustí*   Instituto Cervantes New York

ENCYCLOPEDIA OF CONTEMPORARY
LATIN AMERICAN AND CARIBBEAN CULTURES.

Authors: Daniel Balderston, Mike González, and Ana M. López, eds.

The Encyclopedia of Contemporary Latin American and Caribbean Cultures contains more than 4,000 brief entries in English about society, politics and culture after 1920 in said regions. A quick reference tool, ideal for obtaining abstracts about any subject relative to the contemporary Latin American situation.

▶   *Lluís Agustí*   Instituto Cervantes New York

ENCYCLOPEDIA of CONTEMPORARY SPANISH CULTURE.
Author: Eamonn Rodgers, ed.

Thematic encyclopedia about society, culture, history, art, and politics in Spain from the end of the Civil War until the present. Written in English, it contains more than 700 entries in alphabetical order. Each entry is followed by references, as well as by a complementary bibliography.

▶ *Lluís Agustí* Instituto Cervantes New York

ENCYCLOPEDIA of LATIN AMERICAN HISTORY and CULTURE.
Authors: Barbara A. Tenembaum, and Georgette M. Dorn, eds.

A classic reference work in English compiled specialists of wide acclaim, this 5 volume works includes more than 5,300 entries in alphabetical order about countries, institutions and persons. A brief bibliography at the end of each entry complements the information.

▶ *Lluís Agustí* Instituto Cervantes New York

GRAMÁTICA de la LENGUA CASTELLANA DEDICADA al USO de los AMERICANOS.
Author: Andrés Bello

This is work is not only considered to be the best reference grammar in the Castilian language, but also one of the best ever written in any language.

▶ *Marlenys Villamar* Professor

GRAMÁTICA DESCRIPTIVA de la LENGUA ESPAÑOLA.
Authors: Ignacio dir. Bosque, and Violeta Demonte, dir.

This reference work covers among other subjects: the basic syntax of word types, fundamental syntactical constructions, temporal, aspectual, and model relationships, sentences and speech, and lexical morphology.

▶ *Lluís Agustí* Instituto Cervantes New York

GRAN DICCIONARIO OXFORD: ESPAÑOL-INGLÉS, INGLÉS-ESPAÑOL
= THE OXFORD SPANISH DICTIONARY: SPANISH-ENGLISH, ENGLISH-SPANISH.
Authors: Beatriz Galimberti Jarman, and Roy Russell.

One of the most extensive and complete bilingual dictionaries of the Spanish and English languages. A dictionary of current usage, it contains more than 300,000 words and phrases, and also includes grammatical charts, verb conjugations, examples of private and business correspondence, résumés in both languages, examples email usage and SMS.

▶ *Lluís Agustí*   Instituto Cervantes New York

HISTORIA DE LA LITERATURA ESPAÑOLA.
Author: Juan Luis Alborg

A history of literature in Spanish, organized chronologically by periods, themes and authors. Chapters on Medieval, Renaissance, Baroque, 18th century, 19th century and contemporary literature. Although first published more than 40 years ago in 1966, Alborg's work, in its second and extended edition of 1970, continues to be an indispensable reference.

▶ *Lluís Agustí*   Instituto Cervantes New York

HISTORIA DE LAS MUJERES EN ESPAÑA
Y AMÉRICA LATINA.
Author: Isabel Morant, dir.

This is a history of women from prehistoric times to the present day. Comprising 4 volumes with contributions from more than 30 specialists, it constitutes an essential guide for all those who wish to explore the situation, condition, position, conduct and reality of women throughout history in Spain and Latin America. It contains, besides an index of names, an extensive bibliography about the periods and subjects covered.

▶ *Salvador Vergara*   Instituto Cervantes Chicago

HISTORIA DOCUMENTAL
DEL CINE MEXICANO.
Author: Emilio García Riera

The history of Mexican cinema, one of the best and most important examples of the art in the Spanish language, can count on the most extensive and detailed study undertaken to date about any Hispanic cinematographic tradition. Chronologically and throughout its 18 volumes, Emilio García Riera covers each era by dissecting each and every production therein. This is an indispensable work for any library specializing in Hispanic studies.

▶ *Lluís Agustí*   Instituto Cervantes New York

HISTORIA Y CRÍTICA
DE LA LITERATURA ESPAÑOLA.
Author: Francisco Rico, ed.

A few years ago language professor Francisco Rico began this magnificent work which over time has become a mandatory reference for the history of peninsular Spanish literature. It systematically compiles the best contributions of contemporary critics about every historical period of Spanish literature, including themes, names and works.

▶ *Lluís Agustí*   Instituto Cervantes New York

HISTORIA Y CRÍTICA
DE LA LITERATURA HISPANOAMERICANA.
Author: Cedomil Goic

Paralleling the work of Francisco Rico, History and Criticism of Spanish Literature, about peninsular Spanish literature, the work of Cedomil Goic compiles the best contributions of contemporary critics about all the historical periods of Hispanic-American literature, including themes, names and works.

▶ *Lluís Agustí*   Instituto Cervantes New York

LITERATURA CENTROAMERICANA:
DICCIONARIO DE AUTORES CENTROAMERICANOS: FUENTES PARA SU ESTUDIO.
Author: Jorge Eduardo Arellano

Important reference source that provides brief bio-bibliographic entries for the most recognized Central American fiction writers. The second part "Fuentes para su estudio" provides up-to-date bibliographies of other reference sources, anthologies, literary surveys, and more.

▶ *Claude Potts*   Arizona State University

LITERATURA PUERTORRIQUEÑA:
SU PROCESO EN EL TIEMPO.
Author: Josefina Rivera de Álvarez

Rivera de Alvarez's work is the most comprehensive reference text on Puerto Rican literature to date. From Pre-Columbian mythology, to literary works of the 30's, 40's and 60's, the text incorporates extensive notes that include references to secondary literature, as well as a lengthy bibliography.

▶ *Nashieli Marcano*   University of Akron

EL MERCADO del LIBRO ANTIGUO ESPAÑOL:
UNA GUÍA DE PRECIOS.
Authors: Julio Ollero, and Susana Bardón, eds.

This is a reference work providing guidance for private individuals, booksellers and librarians who at some point may be confronted with the need to monetarily assess tomes in Spanish of great age. The work compiles more than 14,000 entries for book (from incunabula until 1850) and their prices, obtained from booksellers' catalogues. Without having the informative nor organizational richness of the Manual of the Hispanic-American Bookseller by Antonio Palau y Dulcet, it nonetheless helps to clarify many doubts. The work was subsequently expanded in a second volume which covers references to more modern books: From the Generation of '98 to the Literature of the 1960's: A Pricing Guide.

▶ *Lluís Agustí* Instituto Cervantes New York

MUJERES NOVELISTAS y NOVELAS de MUJERES
en la POSGUERRA ESPAÑOLA (1940-1965).
Author: Raquel Conde Pen Alosa

A selective catalog of serious adult novels written by Spanish women in Castilian in the mid-20th century, excluding (most) short stories, genre fiction, and young adult and children's literature. Entries indicate first and successive editions, translations and adaptations, a genre or thematic label, prizes won, brief synopsis, and stylistic commentary. Includes indices of works, chronology, and genres/themes, as well as rankings by number of reprints and prizes won. Also includes brief author biographies and a 21-page bibliography.

▶ *Jeffry Larson* Yale University Library

NUEVA ENCICLOPEDIA de PUERTO RICO.

Author: José A. Toro-Sugrañés

This reference work is a compilation of over 30 years of research, studies and experiences of its contributors. It provides students with a comprehensive source in the fields of geography, history, culture and ecology.

▶ *Nashieli Marcano* University of Akron

ORTOGRAFÍA de la LENGUA ESPAÑOLA.
Author: Edición revisada por las Academias de la Lengua Española.

A useful, clear and indispensable tool in reference to doubts about Spanish usage and style, covering when and how to use capital letters, abbreviations, place names, etc., explained in a precise and relevant way with clear and illustrative examples. The current has been revised by the Academies of the Spanish Language, which is to say, its contents are of common accord with all variants of Spanish in the Americas.

▶ *Lluís Agustí* Instituto Cervantes New York

ORTOGRAFÍA y ORTOTIPOGRAFÍA
del ESPAÑOL ACTUAL.
Author: José Martínez de Sousa

An essential book for every translator and a great aid with everything having to do with the editing of texts.

▶ *Marko Miletich*   Binghamton University (SUNY)

TEATRO ESPAÑOL: (DE LA A A LA Z).

Authors: Javier Huerta Calvo, Emilio Peral Vega, and Héctor Urzáiz Tortajada.

A scholarly encyclopedia of theater of all periods in all the languages (80% Castilian) of Spain. Covers playwrights, selected plays, theatrical concepts, directors and other theater professionals; articles give biographical sketches, lists of major works, and references to the 20-page end bibliography. Also includes lists of entries treating works and terms, cross-references, and an index of works treated.

▶ *Jeffry Larson*   Yale University Library

THE FIREFLY SPANISH /
ENGLISH VISUAL DICTIONARY.
Authors: Jean Claude Corbeil, and Ariane Archambault.

This bilingual pictorial dictionary is an extraordinary tool, which identifies more than 25,000 terms by means of thousands of detailed and precise illustrations. It is organized by topic: astronomy, geography, animal kingdom, plant kingdom, the human being, agriculture, architecture, homes, household items, gardening, home repair, dress, personal accoutrements, communications, transportation. Includes entries like the parts of a faucet in Spanish and their English equivalents, the instruments in an orchestra, the different parts of a sailboat, in short, the names of the reality in which we live, often difficult to describe solely by the words of a regular dictionary.

▶ *Lluís Agustí*   Instituto Cervantes New York

CHILDREN
YOUNG ADULTS

▶ 0 - 5 YEARS OLD   Pg. 159

▶ 6 - 8 YEARS OLD   Pg. 164

▶ 9 - 11 YEARS OLD   Pg. 173

▶ 12 - 14 YEARS OLD   Pg. 185

▶ 15 - 18 YEARS OLD   Pg. 189

0 - 5 YEARS OLD

ANIMALES... SON MUCHOS Y NO SON IGUALES.

Author: María Lucía Carvalhas

These poems are for playing and guessing, for memorizing, for enjoying at home with family or in class. The book follows a pattern: a riddle on the left page and a silhouette of the animal on the right page, with a challenge to the reader to guess the animal or turn the page. On the next page, the reader will find a picture of the corresponding animal and this boilerplate text: "And now, what will happen? Keep reading and find out."

▷ Fundación Germán Sánchez Ruipérez, SOL

COCO Y LA LUNA.

Author: Emilio Urberuaga

The protagonist of this picture book is the perfect prototype of someone who devotes excessive attention to his own interests without worrying about the harm he causes other. Given that all children experience an egotistical stage, the author avers that overcoming the conflictive situation will come naturally and innocently: nothing or nobody will convince them of the importance of being generous; they will learn about their socially incorrect behaviors themselves.

▷ Fundación Germán Sánchez Ruipérez, SOL

LA CUCARACHA MARTINA: UN CUENTO FOLKLÓRICO DEL CARIBE.

Author: Daniel Moreton

NEW

"While searching for the source of one beautiful sound, a ravishing cockroach rejects marriage proposals from a menagerie of city animals which woo her with their noises". (Taken from OCLC)

▷ *Norma Medina Ortiz*　　　Seminole County Public Library System

CÚPER, PERRO VOLADOR.

Author: Montse Ganges

Cooper is a dreamer, an imaginative and naive terrier. He will awaken the interest of young readers because his adventures are full of sympathy, good humor and innocence. This time Cooper's fantasy borders on the outlandish since he can't think of anything else but flying to reach his goal: some delicious cookie. Ganges weaves a delicate story of friendship in which the goal is reached thanks to the support of a parrot. A simple and tender tale.

▷ Fundación Germán Sánchez Ruipérez, SOL

FEDERICO.

 Author: Leo Arias

The main character of the book is a child who tries by all means possible to reveal the mystery of his cat's identity. The child's questions and doubts are reflected in the graphic work, which echoes the text, and narrates in its own peculiar language, the child's sense of uncertainty when facing a cat who does not respond. The work stands out above all for its sense of humor, in reality, the main protagonist of the story about friendship.

▶ Fundación Germán Sánchez Ruipérez, SOL

LA GRAN MONTAÑA.

Author: José Antonio Delgado

Elephant has a dream. He wants to climb to the top of the great snowy mountain, but he knows what a difficult task it is. Camel, Kangaroo and Yak want to accompany him. A precious animal story in which friendship and achievement play a major role. The power of comradeship and the hope of fulfilling a dream are the principal engines for reaching the goal. A book that will encourage children to work together and to try to discover and value the special qualities that each of them possesses.

▶ Fundación Germán Sánchez Ruipérez, SOL

HISTORIA del UNO.

Author: María de la Luz Uribe

This story in verse tells how the number 1 goes out to make friends because he feels lonely. He crosses valleys, rivers and deserts where he finds the rest of the numbers from 0 to 9. The journey is long and is not exempt from disappointment and dangers. In the end, the character-number obtains what he seeks through hard work and effort. Each number represents a different character.

▶ Fundación Germán Sánchez Ruipérez, SOL

EL LORO de ROBINSON.

Author: Antonio A. Gómez Yebra

A boy named Robinson, like the literary character Robinson Crusoe, comes to a desert island. There he experiences loneliness and longs for his family. He recovers some objects from the ship which the tides bring to the beach: a plastic chair, a great piece of fabric from a sail, a black telescope and a tattered novel. Later he makes friends with a parrot. With the help of many others of his kind, the parrot will fly the boy back home. A dream story for the very young that will introduce them to adventure stories.

▶ Fundación Germán Sánchez Ruipérez, SOL

MAMÁ ELEFANTE es GENIAL.

Author: Gabriela Keselman

Mom Elephant feels inadequate because of her enormous trunk and enviously observes other mathers. But her children make her regain her self-confidence because, although she's not able to put on a t-shirt, she can do a lot of good things with her trunk that other mothers without one cannot do. Differences are what make a person special; that's why we have to accept them and find their positive side.

▶ Fundación Germán Sánchez Ruipérez, SOL

ME GUSTA.

Author: Javier Sobrino

NEW

This is a wonderfully poetic book about the small pleasures of life that children experience every day. Using large text and skillful charcoal and paint illustrations Sobrino crafts a lyrical, accessible story about enjoying the air, smelling the roses, tasting delicious sweets, and cuddling with mom. Fantastic book for storytime and a staple for any children's collection.

▶ *Alma Chavarría* Houston Public Library

¿ME LO DEJAS?.

Author: Isabel Abedi

A handsome original narrative that forces the reader to decide where to begin the reading. Two parallel stories, two points of view about a sole conflict, resolved in a common ending. Among the themes covered are the capacity to recognize an error and set it right, empathy and generosity. The characters' behavior and the situation they face are easy to identify for the children, who are aided in the task by fun and dramatic illustrations.

▶ Fundación Germán Sánchez Ruipérez, SOL

LAS MEDIAS DE LOS FLAMENCOS.

Author: Horacio Quiroga

The snakes have invited every animal to a huge party in the jungle. The flamingos are excited, but they don't have much to wear. Jealous of the coral snakes' stunning red-striped skin, they figure out a way to concoct fabulous imitation stockings. This etiological tale from Quiroga's 1918 classic Cuentos de la selva (Jungle Stories) revolves around where the stockings come from and how the coral snakes deal with a just punishment. Dramatic woodcuts convey a sense of the mystery of jungle life.

▶ Reforma

MI CABALLO.

 Author: Georgina Lázaro

 NEW

In gently rhyming text, a boy tells about his hobbyhorse, made from an old broom, yarn, buttons, and old clothes. He describes his imaginative adventures riding the horse, pretending to be an astronaut and Don Quixote. Children who have a favorite toy will identify with the nameless protagonist and enjoy his fantasy play.

▶ *Nellie B. Mulkay*   N Y State Spanish Bilingual Education Technical Assistance Center at NYU

¡MUU, MOO!: RIMAS DE ANIMALES.

 Authors: Selected by Alma Flor Ada & F. Isabel Campoy

 NEW

From around the Spanish-speaking world comes this collection of the sounds of childhood, beautiful in both pictures and words, providing all families with the joyful tools to encourage emergent literacy and a love for books.

▶ *Andrew Medlar*   Chicago Public Library

PÉTALA.

 Author: Pep Bruno Galán

Pétala is a daring pigeon who one day, when she discovers that the water in the forest has disappeared, decides to go up to the house of rain to investigate the matter. There she discovers that a horrible dragon is drinking it all. Thanks to the help of her friends and a good idea, Pétala will bravely confront the voracious monster in order to get the water back.

▶   Fundación Germán Sánchez Ruipérez, SOL

POMELO SE PREGUNTA.

 Author: Ramona Bâdescu

Pomelo, a small elephant, makes a wonderful connection with beginning readers because of the innocence, artlessness and honesty that he brings to his daily life and to changes in the environment. Like any child, Pomelo tries to find answers to his great existential doubts and does so with great tenderness, masterful irony and a delectable sense of humor.

▶   Fundación Germán Sánchez Ruipérez, SOL

EL SAPO DISTRAÍDO.

Author: Javier Rondón

Told in simple rhyming sentences with colorful and dynamic illustrations, this book tells the tale of a toad that makes a list to go shopping and then, due to all the distractions in the city, forgets to buy anything at all! This book contains good vocabulary for beginning students like colors (i.e., verde, morado, anaranjado), food words (i.e., mantequilla, tortillas, mermelada) and fruits (i.e., parchita and tomate).

▶ *Lori Langer de Ramírez*   Herricks Public Schools, NY

SWEET DREAMS / DULCES SUEÑOS.

Author: Pat Mora

NEW

Bedtime routines are a ritual for all parents and children. Pat Mora has created a soothing, poignant bedtime addition to her My Family/Mi Familia series. Bright, crisp watercolor illustrations of Latino families greet the reader as abuelita bids goodnight to the stars, the birds, the pets, and her grandchildren. This bilingual offering is good for reading together and allows Spanish-speaking parents and grandparents a good opportunity to bond with the children in their life.

▶ *Alma Chavarría*   Houston Public Library

 **6 - 8 YEARS OLD**

A LA TIERRA LE HA SALIDO UNA GOTERA.

Author: Agatha Echevarría Canales

An astronaut discovers that Earth has an enormous leak whose effect is manifested in different parts of the planet: extreme drought in African countries, floods in northern countries and other catastrophic disruptions. The adults discuss possible solutions, but it is the common sense of the children that will help implement the truly necessary measures. The purpose of the story is to make us aware of the need to take care of the environment, to use natural resources responsibly, and to recycle waste products. The book includes simple pictograms which make the reading more entertaining,

▶ Fundación Germán Sánchez Ruipérez, SOL

ABECEDARIO DE ARTE.

Authors: Carlos Reviejo Hernández; Ana Moreno Reborditos

This series of poems take the reader on a tour of the history of art based on 29 paintings by great masters from the fifteenth to the twentieth century. The book provides an opportunity to learn to observe the paintings in a fun way, which is completed with a didactic guide to each work. By means of the guide, which includes a series of suggestive questions, addressed to both adults and children, the reader is encouraged to develop his or her imagination and focus on the most important elements. The book may be used as a teaching tool for discovering the select content of the Thyssen Museum before a visit.

▶ Fundación Germán Sánchez Ruipérez, SOL

EL ARCA DE VALORES.

Author: Rebeca Orozco

NEW

This book would be a valuable addition to any Hispanic collection because it teaches values such as responsability, tolerance, generosity, cooperation, and confidence, all of which are of great importance for the moral education of future generations. The illustrations are simple and follow the story closely.

▶ *Enriqueta Kozakowski* Detroit Public Library – Bowen Branch

BOLINGA.

Author: Elvira Lindo

The adventures of a gorilla who tries to understand the behavior of humans. The gorilla was trapped in the wild and taken to a zoo, where he witnesses the often absurd behavior of the human visitors. A lighthearted story interspersed with great doses of humor. An easy to read story which captures and entertains the reader.

▶ Fundación Germán Sánchez Ruipérez, SOL

CARMINA, LA PINGÜINA QUE VIENE DE ARGENTINA.

 Authors: Pep Castellano; Canto Nieto

Carmina is a penguin who has had to emigrate from Argentina with her family because of global warming and climate change. During her stay in her new school, she tries to adapt and get to know her classmates, but the children are always telling her she's very strange. On her birthday, they will all arrange a lovely surprise party her at the marine circus and that way Carmina will feel proud of being so strange.

▶ Fundación Germán Sánchez Ruipérez, SOL

CON LOS DEDOS DE UNA MANO.

 Author: Isidro Ferrer Soria

This original and attractive book contributes a fresh approach to handicrafts. Children are instructed on how to paint using their fingertips dipped in color inks. From this simple idea, and using only an ink pad and their fingers, boys and girls are able to draw amusing characters. This simple and original book is easy to follow and has a notable aesthetic dimension, providing children with a fun way to develop their creativity and imagination.

▶ Fundación Germán Sánchez Ruipérez, SOL

LA DETECTIVE JULIETA
Y EL MISTERIO DE LA CLASE.
 Author: Carmen Gil Martínez

A carefree adventure story in which a girl and a dog who play at being detectives solve the mystery of the disappearances that are plaguing the school. The guilty party is a playful witch who is bored because she has no friends and comes up with all sorts of pranks to have fun. Julieta and her dog will come upon the witch and ask to be her friends.

▶ Fundación Germán Sánchez Ruipérez, SOL

DISCURSO DEL OSO.

Author: Julio Cortázar

The Bear's Speech by Julio Cortázar, presented in this case as a picture book, belongs to his History of Cronopios and Famas (Cronopios and Famas are portmanteau words that describe two types of characters). The bear is a clear example of a cronopio, that is, a being who sees reality from another point of view, who is on the margin, in this case in the plumbing of a building.

▶ Fundación Germán Sánchez Ruipérez, SOL

DISPARATES.

 Author: Gustavo Roldán

Text and illustrations combine in this magnificent homage to fantasy and the literature of the absurd much in the vein of Gianni Rodari. By means of simple rhymed texts, a hilarious gallery of characters is introduced, all equally surprising and moving in their innocent and jocular pathos. This book is full of freshness, good humor, kindness, and fun.

▷   Fundación Germán Sánchez Ruipérez, SOL

DOÑA FLAUTINA RESUELVELOTODO.

 Authors: Yanitzia Canetti; Avi

 NEW

Doña Flautina is a happy woman who can fix any problem in the blink of an eye and dedicates herself to helping others. The clever chapters detail each of her unique, quick solutions and her neighbors' appreciation.

▷   *Diego Mansilla*   Acton-Boxborough Regional High School

EN TIEMPOS DIFÍCILES.

Authors: Yanitzia Canetti; Willy Romont

 NEW

Why can't I buy new toys? Why aren't we going on vacation this year? When times are tough, it is difficult for children to understand why things change. This book follows a family that faces economic challenges, and shows how they overcome them together.

▷   *Diego Mansilla*   Acton-Boxborough Regional High School

EL FLAMBOYÁN AMARILLO.

 Author: Georgina Lázaro

A young boy and his mother go for a walk in the country and are awed by the beauty of a yellow flamboyan tree. After enjoying its company and shade, the child takes one of its seeds with him and plants it. He cares for it over many years and in time the plant grows into a beautiful flowering tree. The watercolor and pastel illustrations support and extend the rhythmic text quite nicely. This uplifting story about the interconnectedness of people and nature makes an enjoyable choice for independent reading and an appealing read-aloud.

▷   *Nellie B. Mulkay*    N Y State Spanish Bilingual Education Technical Assistance Center at NYU

LAS FLORES DE NIEVE Y EL ZORRITO.

 Author: Africa Coll Fernández

This simple circular story introduces a little fox who makes many important discoveries: the happiness which sincere friendship affords us, the sweetness of honey, the fleetingness of things—exemplified by the ephemeral snow which disappears with the heat—and the marvelous perfection with which nature marks the passage of time to complete the cycle of the seasons.

▶ Fundación Germán Sánchez Ruipérez, SOL

LA GATA DE LOS PINTORES.

 Author: Antonio Orlando Rodríguez
NEW

A beautifully illustrated story, where the graphic content is an instrumental part of the narration of events.

▶ *Octavio Núñez* US Librarian

GRACIAS / THANKS.

 Author: Pat Mora
NEW

This delightful bilingual picture book introduces us to a bicultural little boy who reminds us of the many things in life to be thankful for. "For the sun that wakes me up so I don't sleep for years and years and grow a long, white beard, thanks" the story begins. As the boy continues to give thanks for the simple daily things in life he introduces us to his family and friends. The reader will meet the uncle, for instance, while he plays the guitar and the family dances and claps. In another scene we meet some of the boy's classmates as they perform in a play. "For my family, who clapped and clapped even when I tripped on the stage in the school play, thanks" he says. This work is presented in beautiful, bright colored illustrations that enhanced the text and give the reader a clear depiction of the diversity of the family and community. The last page "For the cricket hiding when he serenades us to sleep, thanks" the boy tells us as he prepares to go to sleep. Mora's poetic writing is presented in Spanish and English and conveys a cheerful atmosphere. The author endnote challenges the reader to think about the many things that one can be thankful for. This book will make a great addition to any school or public library. The simple bilingual text makes it a perfect choice to read aloud.

▶ *Elizabeth García* Queens Library

LA HISTORIA del RAINBOW WARRIOR.

Author: Rocío Martínez Pérez

In scintillating words and pictures, Rocío Martínez tells us the story of a ship painted the colors of the rainbow and boasting a mechanical heart created to protect nature. The so-called Rainbow Warriors, the crew of the Rainbow Warrior, protected animals from indiscriminate hunting, monitored the pollution of the ocean or the use of deadly nets. This story will raise awareness among readers about the importance of protecting the environment. The end of the book is a fold-out mural with historical facts about this celebrated Greenpeace ship.

▶ Fundación Germán Sánchez Ruipérez, SOL

LA ISLA VIAJERA.

Author: Antonio Orlando Rodríguez NEW

The protagonists board an island which becomes unmoored and drifts, and later discover a variety of creatures and phenomena. Highly recommended for small children.

▶ *Octavio Núñez* US Librarian

LEO el DRAGÓN LECTOR.

Author: José Andrés Villota Rocha

Taking the well-known fire-breather as a resource, the author of Leo the Dragon Reader changes the role of this mythic animal by giving a twist to the feats usually performed by dragons in stories. Thus, the reader encounters a dragon who, charged with protecting a wizard fixated with reading and books, ends up becoming a great reader and a passionate defender of reading.

▶ Fundación Germán Sánchez Ruipérez, SOL

LUNA.

Authors: Antonio Rubio y Oscar Villan NEW

With its repetitive, reinforcing, and predictable text; charming, naïve illustrations; and gentle mood; this is the ideal board book to read or sing again and again each evening at bedtime.

▶ *Andrew Medlar* Chicago Public Library

LA MARIPOSA.

Author: Francisco Jiménez

This autobiographical story shares how Francisco enters first grade not understanding English. The story portrays his feelings and frustrations, yet positively shows the efforts he makes to learn are successful. Magnificent illustrations are rich in color and expression.

▶ *Dr. Jennifer Battle* Texas State University-San Marcos

LA MÁS DIVERTIDA HISTORIA DE MOZART NIÑO.

Author: *Victoria Bermejo Sánchez Izquierdo*

Mozart's childhood, narrated with self-assurance, is the focus of this illustrated book in album format. Clearly delineated illustrations in vivid colors animate the story, taken from real life but full of curiosities and anecdotes, which seeks the complicity of its readers. Pleasant and visually attractive, the book is easy to read for beginning readers and appropriate for use in the classroom.

▶   Fundación Germán Sánchez Ruipérez, SOL

EL MEJOR ES MI PAPÁ.

Author: Georgina Lázaro
                                                          NEW

In a kingdom far, far away, a time and place has been set to choose the best father of all. In verses, each one of the animals, from a chick to a firefly, from a frog to a penguin, tells why their candidate is the best one. Find out the reasons why everyone's father is the best in the world through this warm and loving tale about relationships between father and child.

▶   *Nellie B. Mulkay*   N Y State Spanish Bilingual Education Technical Assistance Center at NYU

MORRIS, QUIERO UNA PESADILLA.

Author: Gabriela Keselman

On his last adventure, Morris the raccoon will be charged with another exploit: finding a terrible nightmare for Lupino the wolf. Lupino has not been a ferocious wolf ever since he stopped having nightmares. But, where does one find a nightmare? Morris will have to gather together all the horrible things he can in order to make one. The bad thing about horrible nightmares is that they're really horrible. A funny story that is also quite mad.

▶   Fundación Germán Sánchez Ruipérez, SOL

ÑAM.

Author: Puño
                                                NEW

When a city is terrorized by an enormous and horrible monster, a young girl must face the monster and save all the inhabitants. Kids will enjoy the action-packed illustrations.

▶   *Rachel Fewell*   Anythink Libraries

EL OSO CANSADO.

Authors: Concha López Narváez; Rafael Salmerón López

This play is to be staged in two acts. The plot revolves around a tree, a bear, and a honeycomb. All the animals that approach ask the bear to help them get honey and they receive the same reply. The play is structured like a traditional story, with recurring actions, rhymes, onomatopoeias, and word games. The book includes suggestions, addressed to the child, on how to put on the play, make the set decorations, costume the actors and choose the music.

▶ Fundación Germán Sánchez Ruipérez, SOL

 ## PLATERO y YO.
(DE JUAN RAMÓN JIMÉNEZ CONTADO A LOS NIÑOS).
Author: Rosa Navarro Durán

NEW

This story retold by Rosa Durán beautifully illustrates so many elements of Spanish culture and tells the touching story of the famous author and his burro. It is a great book to read aloud in Spanish, chapter by chapter, to children of all ages!

▶ *Ellen H. Martín*   Southampton Intermediate School

 ## PRINCESA va al TEATRO.

Author: Sagrario Pinto Martín

This brief theatrical piece is addressed to young readers who are experiencing this genre for the first time. Consisting of fifteen scenes arranged in sequence and following a linear exposition, the play reveals a plot that, although it may seem strange because of its context, is appropriate to the child's own feelings. Boredom has you in its grip; reading and the development of imagination it inspires may be the perfect cure. In the end, the princess does not go to the theater, but we might go as a form of driving away unnecessary yawns.

▶ Fundación Germán Sánchez Ruipérez, SOL

 ## SOY el más GUAPO.

Author: Mario Ramos

This humorous story book introduces a wolf who claims to be the handsomest creature in all the forest, and all the characters he meets follow his lead and tell him so. All, that is, except the small dragon, who is neither afraid of the wolf, nor places any importance in the wolf's claim. The author, by means of this work that incorporates characters from traditional books like Little Red Riding Hood, Snow White or The Three Little Pigs, wants to demonstrate to youngsters that beauty is relative and not the most important of qualities.

▶ Fundación Germán Sánchez Ruipérez, SOL

DEL OMBLIGO DE LA LUNA.

Author: Francisco Alarcón

NEW

Using his childhood in Mexico as inspiration Alarcón presents twenty-two thoughtful, down-to-earth poems in his second collaboration with illustrator Maya González. The bold brushstrokes of González's art perfectly highlight the bilingual text of each stanza and Alarcón gifts the reader with a slice of insight into his family and childhood. Children will relate to the subject matter and art work making this an excellent choice for introducing poetry as storytelling.

▶ *Alma Chavarría*   Houston Public Library

TARDE DE INVIERNO.

Author: Jorge Luján

There is a fine line between gentleness and sentimentalism which writers and teachers cross all too frequently, forgetting that the child is sensitive but not mawkish. Luján and Sadat avoid rank paternalism by creating a work in which text and image fuse in harmonious communion, transforming this touching picture book into an exquisite song to the tenderness and simplicity of the love between mother and child.

▶   Fundación Germán Sánchez Ruipérez, SOL

TINO Y LA ALFOMBRA MÁGICA.

Author: Antonio Valle

This book relates the story of a boy who thinks that the carpet in his house can take him all the way up to the Moon. To achieve it, Tino invents passwords, devises word games, learns expressions in other languages and even reproduces animal sounds. Once he sees that everything ends in failure, he tries to combine special movements to activate the magic in his carpet.

▶   Fundación Germán Sánchez Ruipérez, SOL

UN CABALLO DE FUEGO.

Author: Fina Casalderrey

This story narrates the beautiful relationship between grandfather Paco, an old teacher who lives in Vilariño, and his great-grandson Francisquito, who's four years old. One day, when the entire region is being desolated by devastating fires, his granddaughter Celia leaves him to care for Francisquito, and both old man and youngster talk about the fires, since anguish cares nothing about age. To lessen it, both of them plant a small tree seedling in a chamber pot, for later replanting in the soil when the fire is finally extinguished.

▶ Fundación Germán Sánchez Ruipérez, SOL

UN REGALO DEL CIELO.

Author: Gustavo Martín Garzo

Two mothers, one human and other animal, misplace their babies due to cumulative exhaustion. Each one finds the other's baby and cares for it as if it were her own. From this anecdote, the author develops an ode to maternity. A beautiful story that endorses the love of one person for another, without distinction of races and cultures, and presents adoption and acceptance as affective options.

▶ Fundación Germán Sánchez Ruipérez, SOL

¡YA LLEGAN LOS REYES MAGOS!.

Author: Georgina Lázaro

NEW

This beautifully illustrated poem voices the excitement of Three Wise Men's Day from a child's perspective. Each verse explores the emotions, traditions, delicacies, and activities of a holiday that is widely celebrated throughout the Spanish-speaking world.

▶ *Nellie B. Mulkay*　NY State Spanish Bilingual Education Technical Assistance Center at NYU

9 - 11 YEARS OLD

25 CUENTOS TRADICIONALES ESPAÑOLES.

Author: Edición de José María Guelbenzu

This anthology of traditional stories from Spain, which includes, among others, The Enchanted Princess, in which a knight becomes a lion, an ant, an eagle and a greyhound in order to discover the secret of the giant who's holding the princess captive, The Little Sugar House, in which two brothers begin to lick the sugary abode, and The Wolf Who Believes the Moon is Cheese, whose main character is a hungry wolf who, tricked by a fox, goes down a well to get a cheese which in reality is the moon's reflection...

Fundación Germán Sánchez Ruipérez, SOL

A una NARIZ PEGADO.

Author: Juan Kruz Igerabide Sarasola

Sofia likes music very much and plays the concertina very well. Her father thinks she has a special gift and wants her to play in the school festival. But Sofia is not sure she can overcome her stage fright and play before so many people, and above all, before the critical eye of Napias, the chorus director, who never smiles and always complains that everybody does everything wrong.

Fundación Germán Sánchez Ruipérez, SOL

EL CABALLO COBARDE.

Author: Felipe Benítez Pérez

In this brief novel, a pretentious monarch commands his subjects to locate the best horse in the world and train him for fighting. Although they do find him, it is not at all easy to make him fight in the battles against the enemy. An interesting reflection on the limits of greed and more specifically on the use of animals in conflicts between men.

Fundación Germán Sánchez Ruipérez, SOL

EL CIELO a tu ALCANCE.

Author: Michèle Mira Pons

The objective of this book is to make youngsters understand, value, and protect the universe of which the earth is part. Facts are included about the atmosphere and pressure, weather phenomena, eclipses, tides, the solar system, constellations, the signs of the Zodiac, the exploration of space, the dance of the Moon, the Earth and the Sun, planets, shooting stars, the Milky Way and other galaxies. Also included are experiments, a test of the sky and a mini dictionary of space.

Fundación Germán Sánchez Ruipérez, SOL

EN EL NOMBRE DE LOS HOMBRES.

 Author: Manuel Nonídez García

Albert Thomas, alias Alberto Más, is a journalist for a magazine devoted to parapsychology. His work—writing an article—leads to investigate the strange circumstances which surround the death of a young woman linked to a religious sect led by a group of persons who take advantage of the beliefs and naivety of their followers. Albert must face dangerous situations and confront very powerful persons when he tries to help the victim's father. Those events take place in parallel with his family life; he is recently divorced and his daughter has been diagnosed with cancer. The denouement of the plot holds in store a surprise that will challenge his beliefs and turn his life around.

▶ Fundación Germán Sánchez Ruipérez, SOL

ESCUCHA MIS MANOS.

 Author: Alvarito Cuevas

NEW

As a librarian, the Spanish-speaking communtiy which I serve has asked for books about sign language. This charming and simple book teaches using drawings that show how to form the letters of the alphabet. There are also photos that show how to communicate using sign language and readers are asked to talk to a 10-year-old Mexican girl with hearing difficulties. This book is for preschool and early elementary school age children and shows another way of perceiving our world.

▶ *Cynthia Eagan* Detroit Public Library - Conely Branch

FEDERICO GARCÍA LORCA.

 Author: Georgina Lázaro

NEW

This book, written in verse and using the cadence and style of Federico García Lorca evokes the spirit and style of the beloved 20th century poet and playwright and gives children a close personal experience with classic Spanish literature in a picture book biography. It paints a picture of the artist as a fragile, sensitive young boy who finds his strength in stories, songs, plays and books. Federico García Lorca celebrates the beauty of the Spanish language and the healing power of words. This is a winner of The Pura Belpré Author Honor Book 2010 and The 2010 Notable Children's Books (ALSC)

▶ *Nellie B. Mulkay* NY State Spanish Bilingual Education Technical Assistance Center at NYU

FEDERICO GARCÍA LORCA PARA NIÑOS Y NIÑAS...
Y OTROS SERES CURIOSOS.

Author: Federico García Lorca

This anthology covers different periods and finds a point of fusion in its simplicity and suggestion of images. Because of their themes and their form, these poems are apt and interesting for boys and girls who are just beginning to read poetry. Calayatud creates, in turn, a parallel visual universe in continuous dialogue with the verses. The work closes with a basic biography of the poet accompanied by photographs.

▶ Fundación Germán Sánchez Ruipérez, SOL

GABIROCHI Y LA ISLA DE LA VIDA,

Author: RR Gruerra
NEW

A young girl of great heart is chosen to make a voyage to a fantastic world. There she will learn all the lost values which she has to bring back to Earth.

▶ *Rafael Pérez Mercado*   Biblioteca Pública Raquel Quiñones

EL GRAN GUERRERO.

Author: Pello Añorga

This picture book develops a fable, involving the atmosphere of legend and laden with symbolism, about enemies who are fruit of our own creation and the peace that is gained upon vanquishing them, by means of self-discovery and liberation from socially dictated roles. This is a story about personal growth with a pacifist message which provokes reflection on the essential questions that concern a human being.

▶ Fundación Germán Sánchez Ruipérez, SOL

GREGORIO Y EL MAR.

Author: Emma Romeu
NEW

This work of fiction is inspired by the maritime adventures of children who immigrated to Cuba from the Canary Islands and who, like the protagonist, wanted to travel the world. The book was written by the author after interviewing Gregorio, captain of Ernest Hemingway's boat in Cuba.

▶ *Nellie B. Mulkay*   NY State Spanish Bilingual Education Technical Assistance Center at NYU

EL HADA ORIANA. EL ÁRBOL. EL ESPEJO.

 Author: Sophia de Mello Breyner Andresen

This book is written in a poetic tone yet without excessive artifice and presents three stories, all with very different plots and reach. On the one hand, there is a fantasy story about good and bad fairies, which extols values like friendship and solidarity and promotes environmental conservation. On the other, there are two brief legends of Japanese origin: one about an immense tree whose shade darkens half the island where it grows; another about a mirror, a mother's legacy to her daughter, so that she will never be forgotten.

▶ Fundación Germán Sánchez Ruipérez, SOL

EL HIJO DEL BUZO.

 Author: Fernando Lalana Josa

The story of a professional diver and his son provides the broad outline the author uses to create a very funny mystery novel which at times comes close to the grotesque comedy of Mortadelo and Filemón. Ernesto's family life shatters stereotypes, as he is forced to live where his father works, in other words, on a boat. His mother, who was more restless, left them to go live with the modern pirate Barbaverde. The author's sarcasm and irony are expressed through Ernesto, whose audacity will lead him to gather the clues that will reveal the dark secret behind the great anchovy factory and help him find his father, who has mysteriously disappeared.

▶ Fundación Germán Sánchez Ruipérez, SOL

LA HORMIGA MIGA... ¡LIGA!.

 Author: Emili Teixidor

This is the latest entry from the "Miga the Ant" series, which is very popular with its readers, and which gained its author the National Prize for Children's Literature for the first title in the series. On this occasion, readers are approached on the subject of interpersonal relationships. The story plays with sensory language and with the surprising relationships between animals of very different sizes, who like each other but don't know how to meet.

▶ Fundación Germán Sánchez Ruipérez, SOL

JORGE LUIS BORGES.

Author: Georgina Lázaro
NEW

An ingenious use of color and rich text depicts the exciting world Borges, considered one of Latin America's best writers, created for himself as a child. Not allowed to run around like other boys his age, he used his vivid imagination to transport himself to far-off, magical places. Selected as commended title for the 2010 Américas Award for Children and Young Adult Literature.

▶ *Nellie B. Mulkay* N Y State Spanish Bilingual Education Technical Assistance Center at NYU

JOSÉ.

Author: Georgina Lázaro
NEW

From an early age, a boy named José knew the importance of education and standing up for what is right. The truly gorgeous illustrations and verse of José richly portray the youth of José Martí who became famous throughout the Americas as a writer and as the hero of Cuban independence.

▶ *Nellie B. Mulkay* N Y State Spanish Bilingual Education Technical Assistance Center at NYU

JUANA INÉS.

Author: Georgina Lázaro
NEW

Beautiful verse and lushly detailed illustrations tell the story of a little girl named Juana Inés who loved to read at a time when women could not go to school - and went on to become the leading writer/intellectual of her day. This portrait of Sor Juana Inés de la Cruz vividly re-creates life in Mexico in the 1600s, bridging the centuries to show us her early life, dreams, and remarkable accomplishments.

▶ *Nellie B. Mulkay* N Y State Spanish Bilingual Education Technical Assistance Center at NYU

JULIA.

Author: Georgina Lázaro

Julia tells, in verse, the story of a girl born into a humble Puerto Rican family at the beginning of last century. With beautiful illustrations, it re-creates the time in which she grew up, and narrates how she became one of Puerto Rico's and Latin America's most beloved poets. Her name is Julia de Burgos and this is her life before she was big.

▶ *Nellie B. Mulkay* N Y State Spanish Bilingual Education Technical Assistance Center at NYU

EL LIBRO DE NEBAL.

Author: Mª del Carmen del Bosque Nieto

The Kingdom of the Tsar Ivan is full of all sorts of riches, but its inhabitants cannot take pleasure in them because there is no joy. One day, the crown prince, an eleven-year old boy named Alexander, finds out from reading The Book of Nebal that in the Forest of Gems is found the sesame diamond, which means "diamond of joy." Despite everybody saying that it is only a fantasy forest, Alexander departs in search of the diamond, thus entering a region where dreams and reality, in equal parts, are blended.

▶   Fundación Germán Sánchez Ruipérez, SOL

LUCHA LIBRE: THE MAN IN THE SILVER MASK: A BILINGUAL CUENTO.

Author: Xavier Garza

NEW

This is a "must have" title for your public library! On his first ever live Lucha Libre event in Mexico City, Carlitos encounters the wonderful world of the Technicos and Rudos. Between the costumes, acting, and action the book makes you feel like you are ringside!.

▶   *Luis Francisco Vargas*   Yuma County Library District

MADDOX DESCUBRE EL CAMINO.

Author: Care Santos Torres

With Maddox Discovers the Way, Care Santos initiates a series of twelve stories, in which twelve boys and girls are destined to meet. Each one of them possesses a gift, a special ability which completes the gifts of the rest. Together they will struggle for the good of mankind, but they have to meet before twelve trimesters pass. Maddox is the guide, the one destined to gather together the twelve and the one who opens the way to the ARCANUS. They are the twelve elect who every twelve times twelve years must complete a mission to save the world.

▶   Fundación Germán Sánchez Ruipérez, SOL

MALEKIN O EL SECRETO DEL ARMARIO.

Authors: Agustín Celis; Alejandra Ramírez

One of the things Cristina likes best is to dream, but to daydream. Such is the case that she thinks that her grandfather is a duke and that his home is Elanor Castle, an enchanted place. There is where she spends her daydream summer vacation. It is July already, there are few days of vacation left, and she begins preparations to get to this magic place and find new mysteries to solve. What our protagonist doesn't know is that this summer, once it comes, she will find a real mystery.

▶   Fundación Germán Sánchez Ruipérez, SOL

LAS MARAVILLAS de una SENCILLA SOMBRILLA AMARILLA.

Authors: Yanitzia Canetti; Ana López Escrivá **NEW**

A little girl is going to throw out her broken yellow umbrella when a cricket points out that it still has many uses. The imaginative ideas of how to recycle the umbrella are presented in equally creative rhymes.

▶ *Diego Mansilla*   Acton-Boxborough Regional High School

LA MERIENDA del SEÑOR VERDE.

 Author: Javier Sáez Castán

The author and illustrator of this picture book is an unclassifiable creator, capable, like the characters of "Mr. Verde's Afternoon Snack," of remaining hidden behind the foliage, or of surprising and fascinating whoever pauses to look. An invitation from Mr. Green brings together Mr. Yellow, Mr. Purple, Mr. Blue, Mr. Brown and Mr. Black. Once gathered at his home, the host reveals the motive for such an unexpected meeting. He has discovered a mysterious poster written in Latin that proposes a surprising challenge and he warns that if they dare to proceed, everything will change.

▶   Fundación Germán Sánchez Ruipérez, SOL

NAIYAKAY: leyendas africanas.

 Author: Severino Calleja Pérez

We know little about African legends created by their cultures and peoples, and this book provides an excellent opportunity for the children to learn more in depth about this essential topic. The legends of Liberia or Mali, or the story from the Afro-Cuban tradition show the close relationship with nature maintained by African tribal peoples. The book includes an excellent essay, "Situation and Context," which places the reader in the social-historical moment when these legends came to light.

▶   Fundación Germán Sánchez Ruipérez, SOL

NIÑA BONITA.

 Author: Ana María Machado

This book is a MUST for teaching diversity and identity issues with students. It tells the tale of a white rabbit who admires the color of his friend's (la niña bonita) black skin. The rabbit does everything he can to become black like his friend (i.e., he drinks black coffee), to no avail. In the end, he marries a black rabbit and they have beautiful babies of all colors. The message and the illustrations in this beautiful story make it a perfect book for use with young and adolescent students.

▶ *Lori Langer de Ramírez*   Herricks Public Schools, NY

LA NOCHE DE LA REINA BERENGUELA.

 Author: Xosé Antonio Neira Cruz

This children's play won the 2004 Lazarillo Prize and may be equally enjoyed by readers and playgoers. The protagonist is Queen Berenguela, an attractive historical character with an aura of legend, who here embodies the need for love and the desire for freedom, and who seems headed for a tragic destiny. An old drifter who takes care of street pigeons is, from his warm and poetical perspective, the person who tells the Berenguela's story to Paloma, a present-day girl who also suffers discrimination from the other kids.

▷ Fundación Germán Sánchez Ruipérez, SOL

PABLO.

Author: Georgina Lázaro NEW

Pablo is the tale of an imaginative boy who loved exploring nature and writing poems, and who would one day win the Nobel Prize: Chilean author Pablo Neruda. Marcela Donoso's vivid illustrations bring Neruda's magical creativity to life, while featuring his actual house and the surrounding Chilean landscape.

▷ *Nellie B. Mulkay* N Y State Spanish Bilingual Education Technical Assistance Center at NYU

PAÍS DE DRAGONES.

Author: Daína Chaviano NEW

Written in a highly poetic style, this book possesses the rare power of enchanting both children and parents equally. The themes of love, friendship, knowledge, homeland, and freedom abound in these stories whose protagonists are dragons from a wide variety of cultures (Spanish, Aztec, Asian, African). All kinds of characters, from Quetzalcoatl to the author of Don Quixote, come to life in these stories.

▷ *Octavio Núñez* US Librarian

LAS PATAS DEL FLAMENCO.

Author: Emma Romeu NEW

Did you know that colonies of flamingos have baby-sitters who take care of the little ones when their parents are away? This is just one of the amazing facts presented in this book about these endangered creatures. Here you will learn about the habits of this beautiful animal, read a story, and see some wonderful pictures.

▷ *Nellie B. Mulkay* N Y State Spanish Bilingual Education Technical Assistance Center at NYU

PICASSO PARA NIÑOS.

Author: Marina García Gurevich

This book takes children on a tour of the life and work of Picasso. The painter explains in the first person the various stages of his life and discusses aspects of the pictorial work which are reproduced in the book. By means of those comments, the artist's different creative periods and the special characteristics of his painting are reviewed. The book includes a timeline of his life as well as a section of visual games related to Picasso's work for the child to solve.

Fundación Germán Sánchez Ruipérez, SOL

POLISAPO.

Authors: Augusto Roa Bastos; Alejandro Maciel

Polisapo is a young toad determined to become a police officer. Full of clever metaphors against intolerance and in favor of the peaceful coexistence of human beings, this story introduces readers to a magical and little known world: the beautiful lands of Paraguay.

Fundación Germán Sánchez Ruipérez, SOL

QUERIDO ENEMIGO.

Author: Agustín Fernández Paz

One day an enormous dog threw Laura to the floor and since then she considers all the dogs in the world to be her enemies. Overcoming fears is an important part of growing up, and to those who face similar circumstances, it will be comforting to see how the protagonist leaves behind her fears as she is won over by the nobility and unconditional affection of the animal.

Octavio Núñez   Fundación Germán Sánchez Ruipérez, SOL

¿QUIÉN SE ROBÓ LOS COLORES?.

Author: Alister Ramírez Márquez   NEW

This story recounts the adventures of Are, a butterfly girl who travels through different kingdoms of colors. Her mission to reclaim the colors' power from the computer of the evil and greedy man named Taya places her constantly in challenging situations.

Nellie B. Mulkay   N Y State Spanish Bilingual Education Technical Assistance Center at NYU

REBECA AL BATE Y DOS CUENTOS MÁS.

Author: Dinorah Coronado   NEW

This book contains three stories about a baseball player girl named Rebecca, a forgetful girl and a hyper boy. Lovely stories about behaviors and how to help young people succeed.

Nellie B. Mulkay   N Y State Spanish Bilingual Education Technical Assistance Center at NYU

LA REBELIÓN DE LOS ARQUEROS.

Author: Jesús Ballaz Zabalza

Juana's parents were the lords of the Castle of Ollares, but one day their lives took an unexpected turn when Vikings laid siege to the castle and subjugated or murdered the inhabitants. Juana grew up hidden in Leira, a nearby village, under the care of Valeria and her husband. But upon turning fifteen, with the memory of her parents as vivid as ever and spurred on by a fortuneteller, she decides to take her destiny in hand. With a poem and a song as her only weapons, she enters the keep and faces the Lord of Brisamarina. Juana becomes the standard for rebel archers and lancers, who do not stop fighting until they recover the Castle of Ollares.

▶ Fundación Germán Sánchez Ruipérez, SOL

EL REY DE LAS OCTAVAS.

Author: Emma Romeu NEW

Recounts the life of the famous Cuban violinist Claudio Brindis de Salas, a black child in XIX century Cuba who was born free and who began his career as a musical prodigy to become a noted concert musician in Paris, while slavery still existed on the island.

▶ *Nellie B. Mulkay*  N Y State Spanish Bilingual Education Technical Assistance Center at NYU

EL ROCK DE LA MOMIA
Y OTROS VERSOS DIVERSOS.

Author: Antonio Orlando Rodríguez NEW

This is a very entertaining collection of poems, which includes the horror and mystery genres, written in a satirical and humoristic tone which combines various musical and poetical styles. A true original in both structure and execution, also distinguished by the rich and luminous language employed.

▶ *Octavio Núñez* US Librarian

SIETE REPORTEROS Y UN PERIÓDICO.

Author: Pilar Lozano Carballo

In this novel, winner of the Steamship Prize, readers enter into the world of journalism in the hands of a group of young and inexperienced reporters, whose hopes are realized when they produce a very personal newspaper. Some of the themes covered are personal effort to achieve what one believes and desires, teamwork, friendship, multiculturalism, and relationships with parents and teachers.

▶ Fundación Germán Sánchez Ruipérez, SOL

EL TÍO BIN FLOREN.

Author: Jesús Mari Olaizola Lazkano

A small accident serves as a humorous doorway to lead the reader into the narrative world fed by the prodigious resource that is The Thousand and One Nights. The rhythm, the characters, the settings and the formulas used by Oriental storytellers are recreated to develop a plot in pure Arab style, masterfully linking some stories with others until finally culminating in a surprising and happy ending, as befits a classic tale.

▶ Fundación Germán Sánchez Ruipérez, SOL

EL TORITO NEGRO.

Author: Antonio Ferres

This piece of juvenile theatre is remarkable for its lyrical effects and subtle social conscience, and for the way tradition and the avant-garde are merged in a text that calls to mind not only folk traditions but also the puppet theater of Federico García Lorca. In addition, the book includes a brief introductory text and beautiful illustrations in the naïve style.

▶ Fundación Germán Sánchez Ruipérez, SOL

TRES AMIGOS.

Author: Patxi Zubizarreta

This is a beautiful tale about the friendship between two very different beings: a cormorant and a salmon. The bird and the fish become friends, and they will be joined by the wind, who tells the story of their friendship and the journey that will lead them to the sea. The author shows us, with an exquisite sensibility, the tender relationship established by the two protagonists and edifies the reader about the power and value of friendship, which trumps any differences that may exist.

▶ Fundación Germán Sánchez Ruipérez, SOL

UN PUÑADO DE SEMILLAS.

Author: Monica Hughes

NEW

This heart wrenching story of Conception, a poverty stricken child who becomes homeless after her grandmother's death makes us appreciate our friends and family. Her survival story with valor, courage, and self actualization could take place in any Latin American country. This wonderfully illustrated book is a reminder of global issues facing children everywhere.

▶ *Luis Francisco Vargas*　　　　　　　　　　Yuma County Library District

VIKINGOS.

 Author: Dolores Gassós

The objective of this book is to awaken an interest in the history and life of the Vikings by means of a brief introduction and twelve subjects that cover, with text and images, some of the most important aspects of a culture that determined the development of the Middle Ages in Europe. Included are a timeline with important milestones in the history of the Vikings and a small compendium of curiosities.

▶ Fundación Germán Sánchez Ruipérez, SOL

 LA VUELTA AL MUNDO EN 80 PÁGINAS.

Author: Victoria Bermejo Sánchez Izquierdo

Around the World in 80 Pages is a homage to Jules Verne. It tells the adventures and incidents that occur to Phineas Fogg and his faithful retainer Passepartout. To win a bet, the eccentric and phlegmatic Englishman decides to go around the world in 80 days, which was not easy in those days of trains and slow-moving ships. The book contains a host of interesting facts and details about many countries.

▶ Fundación Germán Sánchez Ruipérez, SOL

 YA ESTÁ AQUÍ ¡DON INVIERNO!.

Author: Gabriel Segura Soler

This book offers, by means of a child's diary, a broad range of activities to be performed during the winter months. The book is structured on daily activities that include timing the shortest day of the year, building a woodpecker nest, organizing excursions, creating an alternative Nativity scene, building a Christmas tree with umbrellas, and so on, day by day, until March 20th arrives. The book contains a glossary of "strange words you may find in nature," and simple explanations for executing the activities safely and independently.

▶ Fundación Germán Sánchez Ruipérez, SOL

YO, NAOMI LEÓN.

 NEW

Author: Pamela Muñoz Ryan

This is a coming of age story about a girl and her younger brother who are being raised by their great-grandmother. The family ends up running to Oaxaca, Mexico where she reconnects with her father and her heritage.

▶ *Sherry Lord*
Claremont Inmersión in Arlington

12 - 14 YEARS OLD

ATLETAS DE LAS TIERRAS ALTAS.

Author: Nacho Docavo Alberti

This simple yet dynamic novel narrates the challenges faced by Asaffa, an eleven-year old boy, who tries to emulate his idol, the legendary runner of the 10,000 meters, Haile Gebreselassie, who has just been crowned Olympic champion in the Sydney Olympic Games of 2000. The youngster's great athletic gifts should be accompanied by sacrifices he would only be too glad to make, but the reality of his daily life doesn't seem to correspond to his dream of being a champion.

Fundación Germán Sánchez Ruipérez, SOL

AU REVOIR, MARIE.

Author: Tina Olivares

This interesting theatrical piece for adolescents is appropriate for staging in class, since it include stage directions for that purpose. Hugo, son of a wealthy engineer, and Migue, son of the doorman of a building, are close friends, united in their common lack of interest in school. They fall asleep in Professor Lola's history class when suddenly, they are transported to the French countryside in 1789. Under the guidance of the pretty Marie, daughter of bakers in the simple town, they will live through the events of the French Revolution and "return" to class with an enthusiasm that will take everyone by surprise.

Fundación Germán Sánchez Ruipérez, SOL

DOCE PREGUNTAS A UN PIANO.

Author: Juan Cruz Igerabide Sarasola

Written in limpid, beautiful, almost perfect prose, this novel draws us close, in the most passionate manner, to the intense pain of an adolescent who has just lost her mother to a heart attack. There is no palliative for true pain. The traumatized mind of the young girl indulges in fantasy, tolerates music and acknowledges her father, but the emptiness of her heart is so profound that she can only ask questions that have no answers or questions that always end in the inexorable reality of death. Faith is useless and she will never yield or surrender to resignation. This story is as beautiful and as cruel as life.

Fundación Germán Sánchez Ruipérez, SOL

LA ENSEÑANZA DEL GRAN RÍO.

Author: Mercedes Beatriz Wurm

NEW

A book which can be enjoyed by readers of all ages and which deepens our knowledge about the magic which all living beings possess.

Fundación Germán Sánchez Ruipérez, SOL

GASOL POR PAU GASOL.
EL PARTIDO DE MI VIDA.

Authors: Pau Gasol Sáez; Jesús Sáez; Fernando Carreño Ocaña

This biography of the young basketball player, which describes everything he went through to get to the top, becoming the greatest Spanish player of all time in this sport and garnering international recognition for his play. Through this book the reader gets to know Gasol, not only in the professional but also in the personal sphere, from the early years of his life, when he attended school and started playing basketball, to the present day, when he becomes a star in the NBA with the Memphis Grizzlies. The book is full of personal anecdotes, experiences and photographs which draw us closer to this sports figure.

▶ Fundación Germán Sánchez Ruipérez, SOL

EL INVENTOR DE JUEGOS,

Author: Pablo de Santis

A seven-year old boy becomes involved in an extraordinary and intense adventure in which his own life blends into the game that he himself designed, but that was developed by a mysterious individual. A passion for games, a love of mystery and an exciting plot come together to create a magical story, full of adventures and riddles, to which no one can remain indifferent.

▶ Fundación Germán Sánchez Ruipérez, SOL

EL LABORATORIO SECRETO.

Authors: Lluís Prats Martínez; Enric Roig Tió,

Mystery, adventure and a bit of science fiction are the genres which give form to this story of short chapters and fast-paced prose. Two adolescent boys accompany their parents to Paris on a business trip. By chance, they discover an abandoned laboratory, full of sophisticated inventions, one of which is capable of producing terrible hallucinations. The investigative company Trouton wants to use this machine for a million-dollar project and in order to obtain it, they kidnap one of the youngsters.

▶ Fundación Germán Sánchez Ruipérez, SOL

EL LIBRO MALDITO DE LOS TEMPLARIOS.

Author: Francisco Díaz Valladares

This narrative belongs to the tradition of thrillers about secret societies. The author takes a historical episode as a starting point and proceeds to construct a story which builds on those events, creating an atmosphere where mystery and fantasy fuse. With a fast-moving plot, where all loose ends are accounted for, the author uses all the resources of both children's books and mystery novels to rivet the attention of the adolescent reader. At the same time, the author uses historical references which lend verisimilitude to the story as well as a cinematographic exposition that allows us to immerse ourselves in the world he has created.

▶ Fundación Germán Sánchez Ruipérez, SOL

MARTINA Y EL MAR.

Author: Casal Rivas Paula

Martina likes to pass the hours on the beach looking for shells or anything else she can find. She likes it so much, in fact, that she doesn't realize that her family has departed and left her alone on the beach. This is when her adventure begins. A Norwegian scientist helps her and tells her a bunch of stories about whales and the sea. He also gives her a strange tool made from the ear of a blue whale so that our protagonist can discover what it is and how to use it.

▶ Fundación Germán Sánchez Ruipérez, SOL

MENGUANTE.

Author: Alfredo Gómez Cerdá

Humor makes its presence felt throughout the plot of this novel that is part fantasy and part satire. Sometimes the humor is kindly, sometimes it winks at the reader and other times it is unabashedly caustic. This double game frames the fable of the writer protagonist who had to learn to respect himself and his reader so that he could "grow". Yet there's also a place for the resolution of conflicts between father and son and the overcoming of trials by the protagonists, on the basis of courage and noble intentions. All will learn and grow if they join in this fantastic journey.

▶ Fundación Germán Sánchez Ruipérez, SOL

POBRE MANOLITO.

Author: Elvira Lindo

Manolito is back on track with his yarns, about things that only happen to him, or that happen to everybody, only that he tells them with more flair. This is the second volume of his stories about family, the gang and school, possibly the most memorable neighborhood children's stories ever told. Poor Manolito! He really is misunderstood! This is a children's book for readers of all ages, because, as Manolito says, dying before you reach 100 is just not worth it.

▶ Fundación Germán Sánchez Ruipérez, SOL

POR EL CAMINO DE ULECTRA.

Author: Martín Casariego Córdoba

Based on an original idea, this novel is set in a dark future in order to reflect on the none too clear present. It is the year 2314 and some kids try to recover the ability to read in order to give back freedom to human beings. In the Dark Years, people carry a chip in their brain that prevents them from choosing the knowledge they can acquire, since everything is already programmed to the last detail, including the day and time of death. The society is apparently happy, but Miguel Van Horne and Glaster Sanabu will embark, along with the intrepid Flecha, on dangerous missions to find out why their parents have died before their allotted time.

▶ Fundación Germán Sánchez Ruipérez, SOL

¿QUIÉN MATÓ A REGIOMONTANO?.

Author: Carlos Olalla Linares

The German astronomer Johann Müller, known as Regiomontanus, whom the Pope has charged with the necessary reform of the calendar that has been pending since the Council of Nicea, sends a letter to his friend and former disciple Marcus Nero. In the letter, he asks Marcus to visit Rome and he gives a glimpse of the novel astronomical ideas on which he is working. When Marcus Nero arrives in Rome accompanied by his daughter, he learns that his former master has died and decides that the rumors about the strange circumstances surrounding the event merit further investigation.

▶ Fundación Germán Sánchez Ruipérez, SOL

SANTIAGO.

Author: Federico García Lorca

"Naive Ballad" is the subtitle of this early Lorca poem, written mostly in dialogues, based on the ingenuous popular beliefs of humble people who dreamed and consoled themselves with looking at the sky. The influence of a refined modernist aesthetic naturally blends with popular and traditional elements. The wild joy of the children threads the poem like a refrain. The picture book closes with a biographical note about the poet which illustrates his poetics and sensibility.

▶ Fundación Germán Sánchez Ruipérez, SOL

EL VIAJE DE LA EVOLUCIÓN (EL JOVEN DARWIN).

Author: Vicente Muñoz Puelles

Charles Darwin (1809-1882), author of The Origin of the Species (a book which changed the way people thought about human evolution), at age 23 undertook a voyage aboard the Beagle. Years later, he decided to write about the adventures and discoveries of that journey to the delight of his children… and all of us. Expertly adapted by Vicente Muñoz, this book of scientific adventures relates the travels of the young naturalist over the most unexplored places of the planet, from the Galapagos Islands to Tierra del Fuego, and allows us to observe nature through his fascinating gaze.

▶ Fundación Germán Sánchez Ruipérez, SOL

15 - 18 YEARS OLD

EL ALMA DEL BOSQUE.

Author: Manuel López Gallego

The author tackles a problem which may prove very up to date—a maladjusted adolescent whose parents can no longer cope—and proposes a unique solution: the youth is to be sent to a singular reformatory, a place in the forest attended by an old man. Through work and effort, the adolescent's attitude will change and he will value aspects of life which he gave no thought to beforehand, such as the mere fact of chatting with the old man. By means of respect and affection, the old man will produce a change in this youth. Furthermore, the work is replete with intrigue from start to finish.

> Fundación Germán Sánchez Ruipérez, SOL

EL AMOR, LAS MUJERES Y LA VIDA.

Author: Mario Benedetti

This thematic anthology gathers together a selection of the love poems of Mario Benedetti, one of the most brilliant, entertaining and committed Latin American poets. For Benedetti, love is "one of life's emblematic elements. Brief or extended, spontaneous or minutely constructed, it is any form the apogee of human relationships". His poems are informed by that idea. The collection is accompanied by a CD in which the author reads some of his poems.

> *Maripaz García, Ph. D.*   Virginia Beach City Public Schools

APRENDAMOS ESPAÑOL.
DICCIONARIO ILUSTRADO.

Author: Marlene Goodman

Thirty-two categories compile this brightly-colored illustrated Spanish dictionary. Nouns are grouped by topic; adjectives and prepositions are clustered together to show their relationship; action verbs are presented as infinitives; and a map of the seven continents and main bodies of water supplement the text. A detailed index makes this dictionary user-friendly.

> Fundación Germán Sánchez Ruipérez, SOL

LOS ARGONAUTAS.

Authors: Apollonius of Rhodes; Ballester Rafael Escalas

This is an adaptation of the version of Apollonius of Rhodes, who lived in the years 295-215 B.C. Pelias the King is wary about the arrival in his kingdom of Jason, son of the half brother he once deposed, so he sends Jason on a mission fraught with perils, a voyage on the ship Argos to the ends of the world, whose goal is to find the golden fleece in the custody of the cruel king Aeetes. Only with the help of Aeetes's daughter Medea will Jason complete his quest successfully.

▷   Fundación Germán Sánchez Ruipérez, SOL

LAS AVENTURAS DE DON QUIJOTE.

Author: Anna Obiols

The colorful illustrations are comic and almost cartoon-like, almost more appropriate for younger children. However, even teenagers can enjoy this famous story and illustrations. Very short version of Cervantes' story, this story tells about the life of Don Quixote, a gentleman who goes crazy and beliefs he is a knight. It focuses on Don Quixote and Sancho Panza's most famous adventures and briefly mentions other characters as well.

▷   Fundación Germán Sánchez Ruipérez, SOL

EL BLUES DE LA SEMANA MÁS NEGRA.

Author: Andreu Martín Farrero

Intrigue, music and action are three words that define the plot of this novel. The author has achieved a perfect binomial of music and literature by including a CD with jazz music created expressly for the publication. In this way, while one reads the novel, one can enjoy listening to the music and imagine the characters playing it. Andreu Martin, one of the creators of Detective Flanagan, once gain manages to captivate the reader in a police adventure when some young musicians become involved with the drug trafficking mafia and Galician and Romanian drug traffickers.

▷   Fundación Germán Sánchez Ruipérez, SOL

COPÉRNICO.

Author: Carlos Blanco

Carlos Blanco introduces us to the life and work of Nicolaus Copernicus, the 15th century astronomer who changed the image and the concept of the Universe that had endured for a millennia. He describes the environment and age in which Copernicus lived, the Renaissance, a time of great scientific discoveries and innovations. Using two key works by Copernicus, the author analyzes the basis of his heliocentric model, which revolutionized science by postulating that Earth and the rest of the planets revolve around the Sun. Each chapter contains insets which offer definitions or clarify terms, plus a very practical summary of the key elements of the subject under discussion.

▶ Fundación Germán Sánchez Ruipérez, SOL

LA CRUZ DEL DIABLO.

Author: Gustavo Adolfo Bécquer

This legend transports us to that tormented and threatening world common to Romanticism, in which Becquer moves with familiarity and mastery. The suggestive narrative voice invites us to enjoy a story with the flavor of the past, in a magnificently realized setting, which produces a shiver which owes as much to pleasure as to fear. Javier Serrano's impressive illustrations complement the text appropriately with his solid and ominous vision.

▶ Fundación Germán Sánchez Ruipérez, SOL

EL DIARIO AZUL DE CARLOTA.

Author: Gemma Lienas Massot

Family and friends become involved in the troubling topic the protagonist has selected for a school assignment: sexual violence. Everyone helps and contributes real facts, testimonies and personal opinions, which Carlota adds here and there to the pages of her diary. The novel straddles the borderline between fiction and information and combines the protagonist's dialogues with her environment, as well as her personal reflections with the facts obtained for the documentary assignment, a faithful mirror of the chilling reality which informs this issue.

▶ Fundación Germán Sánchez Ruipérez, SOL

GENERACIÓN del 27. POEMAS.

Author: José Antonio García

This collection gathers poems by that generation's ten most representative authors: Rafael Alberti, Vicente Aleixandre, Damaso Alonso, Manuel Altolaguirre, Luis Cernuda, Gerardo Diego, Federico García Lorca, Jorge Guillen, Emilio Prados, and Pedro Salinas. A brief introductory profile of each one is included, along with an interesting study of the group.

▷   Fundación Germán Sánchez Ruipérez, SOL

LOS HEREDEROS de la FUERZA.

Author: María Alamitos

Blanca's memory suffers the aftereffects of the grave accident which put her in a coma for several months. Nothing seems familiar and she thinks that everybody has confused her with another person called Ada. Subsequent events will lead her to assume that identity and live another life. She participates in strange meetings, goes to parties, and even falls in love. Finally, she discovers that the beings which surround her are forces of nature destined to complete a crucial mission. The narrative recounted in the first person by the protagonist, immerses the reader in such a way as to unravel the complex storyline, which mixes mythological elements with elements of the juvenile universe.

▷   *Phyllis Y. Adams, Salem HS*   Virginia Beach City Public Schools

LIBRO de las PREGUNTAS.

Author: Pablo Neruda

This collector's edition, magnificently edited by Media Vaca, provides an excellent opportunity to fully introduce readers both to the poetry and to Pablo Neruda (1904-1973) himself, which are probably impossible to differentiate. This long ode in the form of a question from the great Chilean poet is illustrated by Isidro Ferrer with a kind of photographic collage of rare simplicity and beauty.

▷   Fundación Germán Sánchez Ruipérez, SOL

LA MITAD de tu ROSTRO.

Author: Blanca Alvarez

This juvenile novel, injected with great doses of mystery, recreates the story of some adolescents concerned about uncovering the cause which has led their friend to a state of coma. Friendship, love, youthful rebellion, and the struggle to find the truth are the themes which inform the novel. This story loaded with intrigue will captivate the reader from the very first very moment and touches upon the hidden side we all have.

▷   Fundación Germán Sánchez Ruipérez, SOL

LA NOCHE que WENDY APRENDIÓ a VOLAR.

 Author: Andreu Martín Farrero

The plot of this interesting police procedural finds Wendy Aguilar, a twenty-three year old policewoman, immersed in a difficult case whose resolution will require all her intelligence and energy. A girl called Mon, at the forcible behest of some thieves whose chief is her mom's boyfriend, steals a jewel called the "Eye of God" from a secret room of a mansion. The thieves have murdered the owner at the door and the policewoman investigates the crime. Wendy is taken by surprise by the gang, who try to kill her, but she is braver than even she thought she was, and, after escaping from the gang, nothing nor nobody can stifle her determination to solve such a complicated case.

▶ Fundación Germán Sánchez Ruipérez, SOL

LOS PASOS del MIEDO.

 Author: Concha López Narváez

In these two stories about fear, the author has successfully created an atmosphere of suspense and mystery which maintains the reader in constant tension. In the unexpected and surprising endings, treachery is the order of the day; in the first story the guilty party is a cousin of the protagonist, and in the second, a husband makes his wife's dream come true in order to get rid of her, although his stratagem falls flat and then he meets his match.

▶ Fundación Germán Sánchez Ruipérez, SOL

EL PERSA. ESE DESCONOCIDO.

 Author: El Persa. José Cardona

An unusual sense of humor permeates this book that abounds in surprises of every kind: moving stories, like the heroic exploits in the practices (not very practical) of the port of Pontin-sur-Chailles; astonishing news like the story of the juice snake, who provides delicious juices to her trainer; detailed information about the unbreakable postal ball, a means of communication that traverses the globe thanks to the disinterested collaboration of anonymous kicks; poetic and advertising experiments, a section for motorcycle lovers, and even a cut-out of a plane. A total homage to creativity.

▶ Fundación Germán Sánchez Ruipérez, SOL

SERENA.

Author: Juan Cruz Ruiz

Serena is a restless and intelligent eight-year old girl, who asks questions as marvelous as they are strange, question that her parents are unable to answer because they are caught completely by surprise by them. They are similar to the questions Robien, the other protagonist of these beautiful stories, asks herself. The veracity of the truth, the solitude of being alone, the reality of dreams, music and art… all these questions fan out in this intense book, in a setting which always has the beach, sun and sea as a backdrop.

▶ Fundación Germán Sánchez Ruipérez, SOL

EL PRÍNCIPE DE LA NIEBLA.

Author: Carlos Ruiz Zafón

This chilling story tells about family secrets, outstanding debts and the inevitable passage of time. In their new home, Max and Alicia become friends with a youth. The three friends try to uncover the mystery hidden in their quiet town and experience a terrible and tragic adventure. With precise prose and a swift pace, the author shrouds the drama in a misty atmosphere.

▶ Fundación Germán Sánchez Ruipérez, SOL

EL SIGLO DE TINTÍN.

Author: Fernando Castillo Cáceres

The author analyzes each one of Tintin's adventures following the temporal order in which the different works appeared and creating, at the same time, a parallelism with some of most transcendental events of the twentieth century. There is an evident correspondence between reality and what Hergé included in his drawings, a correspondence which becomes significant both because of the plot, characters, and elements used and because of the absence of explicit references to certain subjects, an absence which may have been deliberate on the part of the artist. This essay allows us to better understand our history through the mind of the celebrated Belgian youth.

▶ Fundación Germán Sánchez Ruipérez, SOL

TURANDOT.

Authors: Giacomo Puccini; Joan de Déu Prats Pijoan

This adaptation the Puccini 's Turandot, provides adolescents a chance to learn about the world of music and history through the eyes of one of its greatest observers, a genius and one of the most accomplished composers of bel canto. The CD included with the book presents a version of the opera by the Orchestra and Chorus of the City Opera of Genoa.

> Fundación Germán Sánchez Ruipérez, SOL

LO ÚNICO QUE QUEDA ES EL AMOR.

Author: Agustín Fernández Paz

Love unites these stories, but love has many masks and may appear disguised as sadness, boredom, passion or even hate. All these disguises appear in The Only Thing Left Is Love. So, intrigue and unease occupy Sara, who receives secret love messages and is unable to discover who sent them. And the serenity of love pierces Ernesto and Margarita with Cupid's arrow. And basically "about love" is the story of a 17 year-old adolescent whose life changes completely when his boss catches him flirting with his daughter…

> Fundación Germán Sánchez Ruipérez, SOL

EL VUELO DE LAS CIGÜEÑAS.

Author: María Isabel Molina Llorente

This historical fiction offering describes a difficult love relationship which highlights the profound differences between the Christian and Islamic kingdoms in the Iberian peninsula during the Middle Ages. Concomitantly, the novel stresses the economic, political and religious motives which might lie behind the pulses of power among persons who shared the same territory. It also provides a wealth of information about many cultural and linguistic elements of the age.

> Fundación Germán Sánchez Ruipérez, SOL

ZARA Y EL LIBRERO DE BAGDAG.

Author: Fernando Marías

This interesting novel cleverly links two wars that are different in appearance but the same in reality, since death is in command of both: the Spanish Civil War and the War in Iraq. A writer wracks his brain trying to begin his next novel when he receives an e-mail in which a certain Max arranges a meeting in order to tell him a valuable secret: the last five words spoken by Antonio Machado before dying in Colliure. Thus, the writer reads Max's autobiography with surprise, while his neighbor, an Iraqi named Waleed, asks him for urgent help, and then he gets to know Zara and the incredible story of the bookseller of Baghdad.

Fundación Germán Sánchez Ruipérez, SOL

AUTHORS INDEX

Abedi, Isabel.
¿Me lo dejas?   Children / Young Adults   Pg. 161

Ada, Alma Flor, & F. Isabel Campoy.
¡Muu, Moo!: Rimas de Animales   Children / Young Adults   Pg. 162

Agustín Goytisolo, José.
Antología personal   Poetry / Drama   Pg. 124

Agustín, José.
Cuentos completos (1968-2002)   Literature / Fiction   Pg. 37
Tragicomedia mexicana: la vida en México de 1940 a 1970   Non fiction   Pg. 118

Aira, César.
Diccionario de autores latinoamericanos   Reference   Pg. 146

Alamitos, María.
Los herederos de la fuerza   Children / Young Adults   Pg. 192

Alarcón, Francisco.
Del Ombligo de la Luna   Children / Young Adults   Pg. 171
Ciclo mágico de las estaciones   Poetry / Drama   Pg. 129

Alas Clarín, Leopoldo.
La Regenta   Literature / Fiction   Pg. 77

Alatorre, Antonio.
Los 1001 años de la lengua española   Non fiction   Pg. 97

Alborg, Juan Luis.
Historia de la literatura española   Reference   Pg. 152

Alegría Ortega, Idsa E., and Palmira N. Ríos, eds.
Contrapunto de género y raza en Puerto Rico.   Non fiction   Pg. 102

Alegría, Ricardo E.
Las primeras representaciones gráficas del indio americano, 1493-1523   Non fiction   Pg. 115

Alemán, Mateo.
Guzmán de Alfarache   Literature / Fiction   Pg. 47

Alfonso X el Sabio.
Cantigas de Santa María   Poetry / Drama   Pg. 128

Allende, Isabel.
La casa de los espíritus — Literature / Fiction — Pg. 29
Eva Luna — Literature / Fiction — Pg. 43
Inés del alma mía — Literature / Fiction — Pg. 53
La Isla Bajo el Mar — Literature / Fiction — Pg. 54
Paula — Non fiction — Pg. 114

Alvar, Carlos; Mainer, José Carlos and Navarro, Rosa.
Breve historia de la literatura española — Non fiction — Pg. 99

Alvarez, Blanca.
La mitad de tu rostro — Children / Young Adults — Pg. 192

Alvero Francés, Francisco.
Lo esencial en la ortografía — Non fiction — Pg. 110

Anaya, Rudolfo.
Bendíceme, Última — Literature / Fiction — Pg. 25

Anonymous.
El Lazarillo de Tormes — Literature / Fiction — Pg. 56
Libro del Caballero Zifar — Literature / Fiction — Pg. 57
Cantar de Mío Cid — Poetry / Drama — Pg. 127

Ansón, Rafael, & Gregorio Varela.
Gastronomía saludable — Non fiction — Pg. 107

Añorga, Pello.
El Gran Guerrero — Children / Young Adults — Pg. 175

Aparicio, Juan Pedro; Mateo Diez, Luis y Merino, José María.
Cuentos del gallo de oro — Literature / Fiction — Pg. 39

Apollonius of Rhodes, Rafael; Ballester Escalas.
Los Argonautas — Children / Young Adults — Pg. 190

Aramburu, Fernando.
Los peces de la amargura — Literature / Fiction — Pg. 73

Archipreste de Hita, Juan Ruiz.
Libro de buen amor — Poetry / Drama — Pg. 133

Arcila, Claudia.
Historias de clóset — Non fiction — Pg. 108

Arellano, Jorge Eduardo.
Literatura centroamericana:
diccionario de autores centroamericanos: fuentes para su estudio. — Reference — Pg. 153

Arenas, Reinaldo.
Antes que anochezca: autobiografía   Literature / Fiction   Pg. 21
El color del verano   Literature / Fiction   Pg. 33
El mundo alucinante   Literature / Fiction   Pg. 65

Arguedas, José María.
Los ríos profundos   Literature / Fiction   Pg. 80

Arias, Martín, and Martín Hadis, eds.
Borges profesor: curso de Literatura inglesa en la Universidad de Buenos Aires   Non fiction   Pg. 99

Arias, Leo.
Federico   Children / Young Adults   Pg. 160

Arlt, Roberto.
El juguete rabioso   Literature / Fiction   Pg. 54

Arrabal, Fernando.
Pic-Nic. El triciclo. El laberinto   Poetry / Drama   Pg. 136

Arreola, Juan José.
Bestiario   Literature / Fiction   Pg. 26

Arrom, José Juan.
Mitología y artes prehispánicas de las Antillas   Non fiction   Pg. 112

Asensi, Matilde.
El último Catón   Literature / Fiction   Pg. 91

Asturias, Miguel Ángel.
El señor Presidente   Literature / Fiction   Pg. 82

Atxaga, Bernardo.
Obabakoak   Literature / Fiction   Pg. 69

Averroes.
Comentario de la Isagogé de Porfirio   Non fiction   Pg. 101

Ayesta, Julián.
Helena o el mar del verano   Literature / Fiction   Pg. 48

Azuela, Mariano.
Los de abajo   Literature / Fiction   Pg. 59

B

Bâdescu, Ramona
Pomelo se pregunta   Children / Young Adults   Pg. 162

Balderston, Daniel, Mike Gonzalez, and Ana M. López, eds.
Encyclopedia of contemporary Latin American and Caribbean cultures   Reference   Pg. 150

Ballaz Zabalza, Jesús.
La rebelión de los arqueros   Children / Young Adults   Pg. 182

Balza, José.
Percusión   Literature / Fiction   Pg. 74

Barea, Arturo.
La forja de un rebelde   Literature / Fiction   Pg. 45

Bareiro Saguier, Rubén,
Ojo por diente   Literature / Fiction   Pg. 70

Barnet, Miguel.
Biografía de un cimarrón   Non fiction   Pg. 98

Baroja, Pío.
El árbol de la ciencia   Literature / Fiction   Pg. 22
Las inquietudes de Shanti Andía   Literature / Fiction   Pg. 53

Barral, Carlos
Memorias   Non fiction   Pg. 111

Beatriz Wurm, Mercedes
La enseñanza del gran río   Children / Young Adults   Pg. 185

Bécquer, Gustavo Adolfo
La Cruz del Diablo   Children / Young Adults   Pg. 191
Rimas y leyendas   Poetry / Drama   Pg. 140

Belli, Gioconda.
El pais bajo mi piel   Non fiction   Pg. 114

Bello, Andrés.
Gramática de la lengua castellana dedicada al uso de los americanos   Reference   Pg. 151

Benavente, Fray Toribio de. Motolina.
Historia de los indios de la Nueva España (1541)   Non fiction   Pg. 108

Benedetti, Mario.
Primavera con esquina rota   Literature / Fiction   Pg. 76
Inventario I, II and III   Poetry / Drama   Pg. 131
El amor, las mujeres y la vida   Children / Young Adults   Pg. 189

Benet, Juan.
Herrumbrosas lanzas   Literature / Fiction   Pg. 49

Benítez Pérez, Felipe.
El caballo cobarde   Children / Young Adults   Pg. 173

Benítez Rojo, Antonio.
La isla que se repite — Non fiction — Pg. 109

Benítez, J.J.
Caballo de Troya — Literature / Fiction — Pg. 27

Berceo, Gonzalo de.
Milagros de Nuestra Señora — Literature / Fiction — Pg. 63

Bermejo Sánchez-Izquierdo, Victoria.
La más divertida historia de Mozart niño — Children / Young Adults — Pg. 169
La vuelta al mundo en 80 páginas — Children / Young Adults — Pg. 184

Bioy Casares, Adolfo.
La invención de Morel — Literature / Fiction — Pg. 53

Blanco, José Joaquín, ed.
El lector novohispano — Literature / Fiction — Pg. 57

Blanco, Carlos.
Copérnico — Children / Young Adults — Pg. 191

Blanco Amor, Eduardo.
La parranda — Literature / Fiction — Pg. 72

Bolaño, Roberto.
2666. — Literature / Fiction — Pg. 19
Los detectives salvajes. — Literature / Fiction — Pg. 40

Bolívar Aróstegui, Natalia.
Los orishas en Cuba. — Non fiction — Pg. 114

Bombal, María Luisa.
La amortajada — Literature / Fiction — Pg. 21
La última niebla — Literature / Fiction — Pg. 91

Bonilla, Juan.
El estadio de mármol — Literature / Fiction — Pg. 43

Borau, José Luis.
Cuentos de Culver City — Literature / Fiction — Pg. 38

Borau, José Luis, ed.
Diccionario del cine español — Reference — Pg. 148

Borges, Jorge Luis.
El Aleph — Literature / Fiction — Pg. 20
Ficciones — Literature / Fiction — Pg. 45
Narraciones — Literature / Fiction — Pg. 66
Obra poética — Poetry / Drama — Pg. 135

Bosch, Juan.
De Cristóbal Colón a Fidel Castro. El Caribe, frontera imperial.   Non fiction   Pg. 104

Bosque, Ignacio, dir, and Violeta Demonte, dir.
Gramática descriptiva de la lengua española.   Reference   Pg. 151

Bosque Nieto, Ma del Carmen del.
El libro de Nebal   Children / Young Adults   Pg. 178

Boullosa, Carmen.
La otra mano de Lepanto   Literature / Fiction   Pg. 71

Breyner Andresen, Sophia de Mello.
El hada Oriana. El árbol. El espejo   Children / Young Adults   Pg. 176

Brown, James W.
Vida moderna hispana   Non fiction   Pg. 119

Bruno Galán, Pep.
Pétala   Children / Young Adults   Pg. 162

Bryce Echenique, Alfredo.
La amigdalitis de Tarzán   Literature / Fiction   Pg. 55
Un mundo para Julius   Literature / Fiction   Pg. 91
La vida exagerada de Martín Romaña   Literature / Fiction   Pg. 92

C

Caballero Bonald, José Manuel.
Diario de Argónida   Poetry / Drama   Pg. 130

Cabrera Infante, Guillermo.
Tres tristes tigres   Literature / Fiction   Pg. 89

Calderón de la Barca, Pedro.
La vida es sueño   Poetry / Drama   Pg. 132

Calleja Pérez, Severino.
Naiyakay: leyendas africanas   Children / Young Adults   Pg. 179

Campobello, Nellie.
Cartucho: relatos de la lucha en el norte de México   Literature / Fiction   Pg. 29

Canetti, Yanitzia.
Doña Flautina Resuelvelotodo   Children / Young Adults   Pg. 166
En tiempos difíciles   Children / Young Adults   Pg. 166

Canetti, Yanitzia & Ana López Escrivá.
Las maravillas de una sencilla sombrilla amarilla   Children / Young Adults   Pg. 179

Carpentier, Alejo.
Los pasos perdidos	Literature / Fiction	Pg. 72
El recurso del Método	Literature / Fiction	Pg. 77
El reino de este mundo	Literature / Fiction	Pg. 79
El siglo de las luces	Literature / Fiction	Pg. 83

Carrera Andrade, Jorge.
Obra poética completa	Poetry / Drama	Pg. 134

Carvalhas, María Lucía.
Animales… son muchos y no son iguales	Children / Young Adults	Pg. 159

Casal Rivas, Paula.
Martina y el mar	Children / Young Adults	Pg. 187

Casalderrey, Fina.
Un caballo de fuego	Children / Young Adults	Pg. 172

Casares Rodicio, Emilio, dir. y coord. general,
José López-Calo, dir., and Ismael Fernández de la Cuesta, dir.
Diccionario de la música española e hispanoamericana	Reference	Pg. 147

Casares, Julio.
Diccionario ideológico de la lengua española	Reference	Pg. 149

Casariego Córdoba, Martín.
Por el camino de Ulectra	Children / Young Adults	Pg. 188

Casas, Bartolomé de las.
Brevísima relación de la destrucción de las Indias	Non fiction	Pg. 99

Casona, Alejandro.
La dama del alba	Literature / Fiction	Pg. 39

Castañeda, Pedro de.
Las siete ciudades de Cíbola: textos y testimonios sobre la expedición Vázquez Coronado	Non fiction	Pg. 117

Castellano, Pep; Nieto, Canto.
Carmina, la pingüina que viene de Argentina	Children / Young Adults	Pg. 165

Castellanos Moya, Horacio.
El Asco: Thomas Bernhard en El Salvador	Literature / Fiction	Pg. 23

Castellanos, Rosario.
Balún Canán	Literature / Fiction	Pg. 25

Castellet, J.M., selec.
Nueve novísimos poetas españoles	Poetry / Drama	Pg. 134

Castillo Cáceres, Fernando.
El siglo de Tintín   Children / Young Adults   Pg. 194

Castro, Américo.
España en su historia   Non fiction   Pg. 106

Català, Víctor, pseud. de Caterina Albert.
Solitud   Literature / Fiction   Pg. 84

Cela, Camilo José.
La colmena   Literature / Fiction   Pg. 33
Cristo versus Arizona   Literature / Fiction   Pg. 36
La familia de Pascual Duarte   Literature / Fiction   Pg. 44

Celis, Agustín; Ramírez, Alejandra.
Malekin o el secreto del armario   Children / Young Adults   Pg. 178

Cercas, Javier.
Soldados de Salamina   Literature / Fiction   Pg. 83

Cerón, Rocío, Julián Herbert, and León Plascencia Ñol.
El decir y el vértigo: Panorama de la poesía hispanoamericana reciente (1963-1979)   Poetry / Drama   Pg. 130

Cervantes, Miguel de.
Don Quijote de la Mancha   Literature / Fiction   Pg. 41
Novelas ejemplares   Literature / Fiction   Pg. 68

Chacel, Rosa.
Barrio de maravillas   Fiction   Pg. 25

Chang Rodríguez, Eugenio.
Latinoamérica: Su civilización y su cultura   Non fiction   Pg. 109

Chaviano, Daína.
Fábulas de una abuela extraterrestre   Literature / Fiction   Pg. 44
Historias de hadas para adultos   Literature / Fiction   Pg. 51
El hombre, la hembra y el hambre   Literature / Fiction   Pg. 51
La isla de los amores infinitos   Literature / Fiction   Pg. 54
Los mundos que amo   Literature / Fiction   Pg. 65
País de dragones   Children / Young Adults   Pg. 180

Cisneros, Sandra.
Caramelo: puro cuento   Literature / Fiction   Pg. 28

Cocco De Filippis,Daisy, and Sonia Rivera-Valdéz, eds.
Conversación entre escritoras del Caribe Hispano: Tomo II Non fiction   Pg. 102

Coleman Alexander.
Cinco maestros: Cuentos modernos de Hispanoamérica   Literature / Fiction   Pg. 32

Conde Pen Alosa, Raquel.
Mujeres novelistas y novelas de mujeres en la posguerra española (1940-1965)   Reference   Pg. 154

Conget, José María.
Hasta el fin de los cuentos   Literature / Fiction   Pg. 47

Corbeil, Jean Claude, and Ariane Archambault.
The Firefly Spanish/English visual dictionary   Reference   Pg. 155

Corominas, Joan.
Diccionario crítico etimológico castellano e hispánico. Reference   Pg. 146

Coronado, Dinorah.
Soy campeón   Literature / Fiction   Pg. 85
Rebeca al bate y dos cuentos más   Children / Young Adults Pg. 181

Cortázar, Julio.
Historias de famas y cronopios   Literature / Fiction   Pg. 51
Cuentos completos   Literature / Fiction   Pg. 37
Rayuela   Literature / Fiction   Pg. 77
Discurso del oso   Children / Young Adults Pg. 165

Cortés, Hernán.
Cartas de relación (1519-1526)   Non fiction   Pg. 100

Cozarinsky, Edgardo.
El rufián moldavo   Literature / Fiction   Pg. 80
La novia de Odessa   Literature / Fiction   Pg. 68

Cruz Ruiz, Juan.
Serena   Children / Young Adults Pg. 194

Cruz, Sor Juana Inés de la.
Respuesta a Sor Filotea   Non fiction   Pg. 117

Cruz, San Juan de la.
Obras escogidas   Poetry / Drama   Pg. 135

Cuauhtemoc Sánchez, Carlos.
Juventud en éxtasis   Literature / Fiction   Pg. 55

Cuevas, Alvarito.
Escucha mis manos   Children / Young Adults Pg. 174

D

d'Ors, Eugeni.
La Bien Plantada   Non fiction   Pg. 98

Dalton, Roque.
Las historias prohibidas del Pulgarcito — Non fiction — Pg. 108
Poemas clandestinos — Poetry / Drama — Pg. 136

Darío, Rubén.
Azul — Poetry / Drama — Pg. 125
Azul; España contemporanea; Cantos de vida y esperanza — Poetry / Drama — Pg. 126
Cantos de vida y esperanza — Poetry / Drama — Pg. 128
Prosas profanas — Poetry / Drama — Pg. 139

Deive, Carlos Esteban.
La esclavitud del negro en Santo Domingo — Non fiction — Pg. 106
Vudú y magia en Santo Domingo — Non fiction — Pg. 120

Delgado, Jane.
La Guia de Salud: Consejos y respuestas para la mujer latina — Non fiction — Pg. 107

Delgado, José Antonio.
La gran montaña — Children / Young Adults — Pg. 160

Delibes, Miguel.
Cinco horas con Mario — Literature / Fiction — Pg. 32

Díaz Alfaro, Abelardo.
Terrazo — Literature / Fiction — Pg. 87

Díaz Eterovic, Ramón.
Los siete hijos de Simenon — Literature / Fiction — Pg. 82

Díaz Valladares, Francisco.
El libro maldito de los templarios — Children / Young Adults — Pg. 187

Díez, Luis Mateo.
El oscurecer — Literature / Fiction — Pg. 71

Docavo Alberti, Nacho.
Atletas de las Tierras Altas — Children / Young Adults — Pg. 185

Donoso, José.
El obsceno pájaro de la noche — Literature / Fiction — Pg. 69

Dorfman, Ariel.
La muerte y la doncella — Literature / Fiction — Pg. 64

E

Echevarría Canales, Agatha.
A la Tierra le ha salido una gotera — Children / Young Adults — Pg. 164

Eco, Umberto.
En qué creen los que no creen   Poetry / Drama   Pg. 131

Edición revisada por las Academias de la Lengua Española.
Ortografía de la lengua española   Reference   Pg. 154

Edwards, Jorge.
Persona non grata   Non fiction   Pg. 115

El Persa. Cardona, José
El Persa. Ese desconocido   Children / Young Adults   Pg. 193

Elizondo, Salvador.
Farabeuf   Literature / Fiction   Pg. 44

Eloy Martínez, Tomás.
El vuelo de la reina   Literature / Fiction   Pg. 94

Enrigue, Álvaro.
Hipotermia   Literature / Fiction   Pg. 50

Ercilla, Alonso de.
La Araucana   Non fiction   Pg. 97

Escobar Golderos, Mario.
Conspiración Maine   Literature / Fiction   Pg. 34

Eslava Galán, Juan.
En busca del unicornio   Literature / Fiction   Pg. 27

España, Claudio, ed.
Cine argentino   Reference   Pg. 145

Espinosa, Miguel.
Escuela de mandarines   Literature / Fiction   Pg. 43

Espriu, Salvador.
La piel de toro   Poetry / Drama   Pg. 136

Esquivel, Laura.
Como agua para chocolate   Literature / Fiction   Pg. 34

Estévez, Abilio.
Tuyo es el reino   Literature / Fiction   Pg. 90

Eustaquio Rivera, José.
La vorágine   Literature / Fiction   Pg. 93

F

Falcones, Ildefonso.
La catedral del mar — Literature / Fiction — Pg. 30
La mano de Fátima — Literature / Fiction — Pg. 60

Fernández Cubas, Cristina.
Todos los cuentos. — Literature / Fiction — Pg. 88

Fernández Paz, Agustín.
Querido enemigo — Children / Young Adults — Pg. 181
Lo único que queda es el amor — Children / Young Adults — Pg. 195

Fernández, Coll.
Las flores de nieve y el zorrito — Children / Young Adults — Pg. 167

Ferré, Rosario.
La casa de la laguna — Literature / Fiction — Pg. 29
Maldito amor — Literature / Fiction — Pg. 59

Ferrer Soria, Isidro.
Con los dedos de una mano — Children / Young Adults — Pg. 165

Ferres, Antonio.
El Torito Negro — Children / Young Adults — Pg. 183

Flores Galindo, Alberto.
Buscando un Inca: identidad y utopía en los Andes — Non fiction — Pg. 99

Fontanarrosa, Roberto
El mundo ha vivido equivocado — Literature / Fiction — Pg. 65

Fraile Prieto,Teresa.
Música de cine en España : Señas de identidad en la banda sonora contemporánea — Non fiction — Pg. 112

Franco, Jorge.
Melodrama — Literature / Fiction — Pg. 62
Paraíso Travel — Literature / Fiction — Pg. 72
Rosario Tijeras — Literature / Fiction — Pg. 80

Fuentes, Norberto.
Condenados de Condado — Literature / Fiction — Pg. 34

Fuentes, Eugenio.
Las manos del pianista — Literature / Fiction — Pg. 60

Fuentes, Carlos.
La muerte de Artemio Cruz — Literature / Fiction — Pg. 64

Fuguet, Alberto.
Cortos   Literature / Fiction   Pg. 36
Mala onda   Literature / Fiction   Pg. 59

G

Galeano, Eduardo.
Las venas abiertas de América Latina.   Non fiction   Pg. 118

Galimberti Jarman, Beatriz, and Roy Russell.
Gran diccionario Oxford: español-inglés, inglés-español =
The Oxford Spanish Dictionary: Spanish-English, English-Spanish   Reference   Pg. 152

Gallegos, Rómulo.
Doña Bárbara   Literature / Fiction   Pg. 41

Gamoneda, Antonio.
El libro del frío   Poetry / Drama   Pg. 131

Ganges, Montse.
Cúper, perro volador   Children / Young Adults   Pg. 159

Gaos, Vicente, ed.
Antología del grupo poético de 1927   Poetry / Drama   Pg. 124

García Gurevich, Marina.
Picasso para niños   Children / Young Adults   Pg. 181

García Lorca, Federico.
Antología poética   Poetry / Drama   Pg. 124
Bodas de sangre   Poetry / Drama   Pg. 126
La casa de Bernarda Alba   Poetry / Drama   Pg. 128
Poeta en Nueva York   Poetry / Drama   Pg. 139
Romancero Gitano   Poetry / Drama   Pg. 140
Federico García Lorca para niños y niñas... y otros seres curiosos   Children / Young Adults   Pg. 175
Santiago   Children / Young Adults   Pg. 188

García Márquez, Gabriel.
El amor en los tiempos del cólera   Literature / Fiction   Pg. 21
Cien años de soledad   Literature / Fiction   Pg. 31
El coronel no tiene quien le escriba   Literature / Fiction   Pg. 35
Del amor y otros demonios   Literature / Fiction   Pg. 39
Vivir para contarla   Non fiction   Pg. 120

García Morales, Adelaida.
El Sur; seguido de Bene   Literature / Fiction   Pg. 86

García Ortega, Adolfo.
Café Hugo   Literature / Fiction   Pg. 27

García Pavón, Francisco.
El reinado de Witiza   Literature / Fiction   Pg. 78

García Riera, Emilio.
Historia documental del cine mexicano   Reference   Pg. 152

García, José Antonio.
Generación del 27. Poemas   Children / Young Adults   Pg. 192

García Badell, Regino.
Tesoros de la poesía en la lengua castellana   Poetry / Drama   Pg. 141

Gardea, Jesús.
Reunión de cuentos   Literature / Fiction   Pg. 79

Garmendia, Salvador.
Memorias de Altagracia   Literature / Fiction   Pg. 62

Garza, Xavier.
Lucha Libre: The Man in the Silver Mask: A Bilingual Cuento   Children / Young Adults   Pg. 178

Gasol Sáez, Pau; Sáez, Jesús; Carreño Ocaña, Fernando.
Gasol por Pau Gasol. El partido de mi vida   Children / Young Adults   Pg. 186

Gassós, Dolores.
Vikingos   Children / Young Adults   Pg. 184

Gibson, Ian.
Federico García Lorca   Non fiction   Pg. 106

Gil de Biedma, Jaime.
El argumento de la obra: correspondencia (1951-1989)   Non fiction   Pg. 97
Poemas postumos   Poetry / Drama   Pg. 137

Gil Martínez, Carmen.
La detective Julieta y el misterio de la clase   Children / Young Adults   Pg. 165

Giménez Bartlett, Alicia.
Muertos de papel   Literature / Fiction   Pg. 64

Gironella, José María.
Los cipreses creen en Dios   Literature / Fiction   Pg. 32

Goic, Cedomil.
Historia y crítica de la literatura hispanoamericana   Reference   Pg. 153

Gómez Cerdá, Alfredo.
Menguante   Children / Young Adults   Pg. 187

Gómez de Avellaneda, Gertrudis.
Sab   Literature / Fiction   Pg. 81

Gómez Yebra, Antonio A.
El loro de Robinson   Children / Young Adults   Pg. 160

Gómez, Sergio.
Buenas noches a todos   Literature / Fiction   Pg. 27

Góngora, Luis de.
Poesías   Poetry / Drama   Pg. 139
Sonetos   Poetry / Drama   Pg. 140

González Iglesias, Juan Antonio.
Del lado del amor   Poetry / Drama   Pg. 130

González Ledesma, Francisco.
Crónica sentimental en rojo   Literature / Fiction   Pg. 36
Soldados   Literature / Fiction   Pg. 83

González, José Luis.
El país de cuatro pisos y otros ensayos   Non fiction   Pg. 109

González, Ángel.
Palabra sobre palabra: obra completa (1956-2001)   Poetry / Drama   Pg. 136

González, Juan Sebastián.
100 Cartas Personales   Reference   Pg. 145

Goodman, Marlene.
Aprendamos Español. Diccionario Ilustrado   Children / Young Adults   Pg. 189

Goytisolo, Juan.
Tríptico del mal: Señas de identidad; Don Julián ; Juan sin tierra   Literature / Fiction   Pg. 89
Campos de Níjar   Non fiction   Pg. 100

Gracián, Baltasar.
Oráculo manual y arte de prudencia   Non fiction   Pg. 113

Granados, Manuel.
Adire y el tiempo roto   Literature / Fiction   Pg. 20

Gruerra, RR.
Gabirochi y la isla de la vida   Children / Young Adults   Pg. 175

Guaman Poma de Ayala, Felipe.
El primer nueva corónica y buen gobierno   Non fiction   Pg. 115

Guelbenzu, José María, ed.
25 cuentos tradicionales españoles   Children / Young Adults   Pg. 173

Guillén, Nicolás.
Sóngoro cosongo   Poetry / Drama   Pg. 141

Gullón, Ricardo, dir.
Diccionario de la literatura española e hispanoamericana   Reference   Pg. 147

Gutiérrez, Pedro Juan.
Trilogía sucia de La Habana   Literature / Fiction   Pg. 89

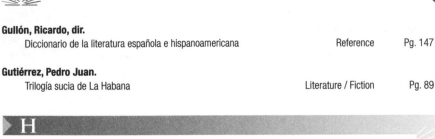

Hernández, Felisberto.
Nadie encendía las lámparas   Literature / Fiction   Pg. 66

Hernández, Miguel.
Cancionero y romancero de ausencias   Poetry / Drama   Pg. 127

Hierro, José.
Cuaderno de Nueva York   Poetry / Drama   Pg. 129

Hiriart, Hugo.
Cómo leer y escribir poesía   Non fiction   Pg. 101

Hirota, Twiggy, ed.
Diccionario de escritores en lengua castellana
quién es quién hoy en las letras españolas   Reference   Pg. 147

Huerta Calvo, Javier, Emilio Peral Vega, and Héctor Urzáiz Tortajada.
Teatro español: (de la A a la Z)   Reference   Pg. 155

Hughes, Monica.
Un Puñado de Semillas   Children / Young Adults   Pg. 183

Huidobro, Vicente.
Altazor o el viaje en paracaídas   Poetry / Drama   Pg. 123

Hurtado Albir, Amparo.
Enseñar a traducir: metodología en la formación de traductores e intérpretes   Non fiction   Pg. 105
Traducción y traductología. Introducción a la traductología   Non fiction   Pg. 117

Ibarbourou, Juana de.
Las lenguas de diamante   Poetry / Drama   Pg. 132

Ibargüengoitia, Jorge.
Dos crímenes   Literature / Fiction   Pg. 41

Igerabide Sarasola, Juan Kruz.
A una nariz pegado   Children / Young Adults   Pg. 173
Doce preguntas a un piano   Children / Young Adults   Pg. 185

Imbert Brugal, Carmen.
Distinguida Señora   Literature / Fiction   Pg. 40

J

Jarque, Fietta.
Yo me perdono   Literature / Fiction   Pg. 94

Jarvis, Ana C.; Lebredo, Raquel and Mena Ayllón, Francisco.
Aventuras literarias   Literature / Fiction   Pg. 24

Jesús, Santa Teresa de.
El castillo interior o las moradas   Poetry / Drama   Pg. 129

Jiménez, Francisco.
La mariposa   Children / Young Adults   Pg. 168
Más allá de mi   Non fiction   Pg. 110

Jiménez, Juan Ramón.
Animal de fondo   Poetry / Drama   Pg. 123

Jitrik, Noé.
Mares del sur   Literature / Fiction   Pg. 60

Juan Manuel, Infante de Castilla.
El libro del Conde Lucanor   Literature / Fiction   Pg. 57

K

Kahlo, Frida.
Escrituras de Frida Kahlo   Non fiction   Pg. 106

Kanellos, Nicolás ed.
Herencia: The Anthology of Hispanic Literature of the United States   Literature / Fiction   Pg. 48

Kattan Ibarra, Juan.
Perspectivas culturales de Hispanoamérica   Non fiction   Pg. 115

Keselman, Gabriela
Mamá elefante es genial   Children / Young Adults   Pg. 161
Morris, quiero una pesadilla   Children / Young Adults   Pg. 169

Kiyosaki, Robert T.
Padre Rico, Padre Pobre   Non fiction   Pg. 114

Kuri Aldana, Mario, and Vicente Mendoza Martínez.
Cancionero popular mexicano   Non fiction   Pg. 100

L

Laforet, Carmen.
Nada   Literature / Fiction   Pg. 66

Laguerre, Enrique.
Residuos de los tiempos   Poetry / Drama   Pg. 140

Lalana Josa, Fernando.
El hijo del Buzo   Children / Young Adults Pg. 176

Lantigua, José Rafael.
Semblanzas del corazón   Literature / Fiction   Pg. 81

Larra, Mariano José de.
Artículos   Non fiction   Pg. 98

Larrea, Juan.
Versión Celeste   Poetry / Drama   Pg. 142

Lastra, Pedro.
Noticias del Extranjero   Poetry / Drama   Pg. 134

Lázaro Carreter, Fernando.
El dardo en la palabra   Non fiction   Pg. 104

Lázaro, Georgina.
Mi caballo   Children / Young Adults Pg. 162
¡Ya llegan los Reyes Magos!   Children / Young Adults Pg. 172
El flamboyán amarillo   Children / Young Adults Pg. 166
El mejor es mi papá   Children / Young Adults Pg. 169
Federico García Lorca   Children / Young Adults Pg. 174
Jorge Luis Borges   Children / Young Adults Pg. 177
José   Children / Young Adults Pg. 177
Juana Inés   Children / Young Adults Pg. 177
Julia   Children / Young Adults Pg. 177
Pablo   Children / Young Adults Pg. 180

Lemebel, Pedro.
Tengo miedo torero   Literature / Fiction   Pg. 86

León, María Teresa.
Memoria de la melancolía   Non fiction   Pg. 110

León, Fray Luis de.
Poesía   Poetry / Drama   Pg. 138

Lezama Lima, José.
Paradiso   Literature / Fiction   Pg. 72

Lienas Massot, Gemma.
El diario azul de Carlota   Children / Young Adults   Pg. 191

Lindo, Elvira.
Una palabra tuya   Literature / Fiction   Pg. 91
Bolinga   Children / Young Adults   Pg. 164
Pobre Manolito   Children / Young Adults   Pg. 187

López de Mendoza, Iñigo, Marqués de.
Obra poética   Poetry / Drama   Pg. 135

López Gallego, Manuel.
El alma del bosque   Children / Young Adults   Pg. 189

López Guix, Gabriel, and J. Minnet Wilkinson.
Manual de traducción Inglés / Castellano   Non fiction   Pg. 110

López Narváez, Concha; Salmerón López, Rafael.
El oso cansado   Children / Young Adults   Pg. 170

López Narváez, Concha.
Los pasos del miedo   Children / Young Adults   Pg.193

López y Fuentes, Gregorio.
El Indio   Literature / Fiction   Pg. 52

Lozano Carballo, Pilar.
Siete reporteros y un periódico   Children / Young Adults   Pg. 182

Luis Sampedro, José.
La sonrisa etrusca   Literature / Fiction   Pg. 85

Luján, Jorge.
Tarde de invierno   Children / Young Adults   Pg. 171

Llamazares, Julio.
La lluvia amarilla   Literature / Fiction   Pg. 58

M

Machado, Antonio.
Antología poética   Poetry / Drama   Pg. 125
Campos de Castilla   Poetry / Drama   Pg. 127

Machado, Ana María.
Niña bonita — Children / Young Adults — Pg. 179

Madrid, Juan.
Dias contados — Literature / Fiction — Pg. 40

Manrique, Jorge.
Poesía — Poetry / Drama — Pg. 137

March, Ausiàs.
Poesía — Poetry / Drama — Pg. 138

Marías, Javier.
Corazón tan blanco — Literature / Fiction — Pg. 35
Mañana en la batalla, piensa en mi — Literature / Fiction — Pg. 60
Tu rostro mañana — Literature / Fiction — Pg. 90

Marías, Fernando.
Zara y el librero de Bagdag — Children / Young Adults — Pg. 196

Marsé, Juan.
Si te dicen que caí — Literature / Fiction — Pg. 82

Martí, José.
Versos libres — Poetry / Drama — Pg. 142

Martín Farrero, Andreu.
El blues de la semana más negra — Children / Young Adults — Pg. 190
La noche que Wendy aprendió a volar — Children / Young Adults — Pg. 193

Martín Gaite, Carmen.
El cuarto de atrás — Literature / Fiction — Pg. 37
Nubosidad variable — Literature / Fiction — Pg. 68

Martín Garzo, Gustavo.
Un regalo del cielo — Children / Young Adults — Pg. 172

Martín Moreno, Francisco.
México Ante Dios. — Literature / Fiction — Pg. 62

Martín Vivaldi, Gonzalo.
Curso de redacción. Teoría y práctica de la composición y del estilo — Non fiction — Pg. 103

Martínez de Sousa, José.
Ortografía y ortotipografía del español actual — Reference — Pg. 155

Martínez Pérez, Rocío.
La historia del Rainbow Warrior — Children / Young Adults — Pg. 168

Martínez Reverte, Jorge.
Gálvez y el cambio del cambio — Literature / Fiction — Pg. 46

Martínez, Guillermo.
La mujer del maestro — Literature / Fiction — Pg. 55

Martínez, Rubén.
Cruzando la frontera: la crónica implacable de una familia mexicana que emigra a Estados Unidos — Non fiction — Pg. 103

Martorell, Joanot.
Tirant lo Blanc — Literature / Fiction — Pg. 88

Mastretta, Angeles.
Arráncame la vida — Literature / Fiction — Pg. 22
Mujeres de ojos grandes — Literature / Fiction — Pg. 64

Matto de Turner, Clorinda.
Aves sin nido — Literature / Fiction — Pg. 24

Max.
Hechos, dichos, occurrencias y andanzas de Bardín el Superrealista — Literature / Fiction — Pg. 48

Mejía, José ed.
Los centroamericanos: antología de cuentos — Literature / Fiction — Pg. 30

Méndez, Alberto.
Los girasoles ciegos — Literature / Fiction — Pg. 46

Mendoza, Elmer.
Balas de plata — Literature / Fiction — Pg. 24

Mendoza, Eduardo.
La ciudad de los prodigios — Literature / Fiction — Pg. 32
El misterio de la cripta embrujada — Literature / Fiction — Pg. 63
La verdad sobre el caso Savolta — Literature / Fiction — Pg. 92

Migoya, Hernán y Marín, Joan M..
Olimpita — Literature / Fiction — Pg. 70

Millás, Juan José.
El mundo — Literature / Fiction — Pg. 65

Mira Pons, Michèle.
El cielo a tu alcance — Children / Young Adults — Pg. 173

Mistral, Gabriela.
Tala — Poetry / Drama — Pg. 141

Molina Llorente, María Isabel.
El vuelo de las cigüeñas — Children / Young Adults — Pg. 195

Molina, Tirso de.
El burlador de Sevilla — Poetry / Drama — Pg. 126

Moliner, María.
Diccionario del uso del español   Reference   Pg. 148

Monsiváis, Carlos, ed.
Lo fugitivo permanece. 20 cuentos mexicanos   Literature / Fiction   Pg. 58

Montejo, Eugenio.
El azul de la tierra   Poetry / Drama   Pg. 126

Montero, Rosa.
El corazón del tártaro   Literature / Fiction   Pg. 35
La Historia del Rey Transparente   Literature / Fiction   Pg. 51

Monterroso, Augusto.
Obras completas (y otros cuentos)   Literature / Fiction   Pg. 69

Monzo, Quim.
Ochenta y seis cuentos   Literature / Fiction   Pg. 69

Mora, Pat.
Sweet Dreams/Dulces Sueños   Children / Young Adults   Pg. 163
Gracias/Thanks   Children / Young Adults   Pg. 167

Moral, Rafael del.
Enciclopedia de la novela española   Reference   Pg. 150

Morant, Isabel, dir.
Historia de las mujeres en España y América Latina   Reference   Pg.152

Moreton, Daniel.
La Cucaracha Martina: un cuento folklórico del Caribe   Children / Young Adults   Pg. 159

Mujica Lainez, Manuel.
Bomarzo   Literature / Fiction   Pg. 26
El unicornio   Literature / Fiction   Pg. 92
Misteriosa Buenos Aires   Literature / Fiction   Pg. 63

Mullen, Edward J. and John E. Garganigo.
El cuento hispánico: A graded Literary Anthology   Literature / Fiction   Pg. 37

Muñoz Molina, Antonio.
El viento de la luna   Literature / Fiction   Pg. 93

Muñoz Puelles, Vicente.
El viaje de la evolución (El joven Darwin)   Children / Young Adults   Pg. 188

Muñoz Ryan, Pamela.
Yo, Naomi León   Children / Young Adults   Pg. 184

Muñoz-Alonso López, Agustín, ed.
Teatro español de vanguardia.   Poetry / Drama   Pg. 141

Mutis, Álvaro.
La última escala del Tramp Steamer   Literature / Fiction   Pg. 56

N

Nava, Michael.
El chico de oro   Literature / Fiction   Pg. 31

Navarro Durán, Rosa.
Platero y Yo (de Juan Ramón Jiménez contado a los niños)   Children / Young Adults   Pg. 170

Navarro, Justo.
Hermana muerte.   Literature / Fiction   Pg. 48

Nazario, Sonia.
La travesía de Enrique   Non fiction   Pg. 118

Neira Cruz, Xosé Antonio.
La noche de la reina Berenguela   Children / Young Adults   Pg. 180

Neruda, Pablo.
Confieso que he vivido   Non fiction   Pg. 102
Canto general   Poetry / Drama   Pg. 128
Cien sonetos de amor   Poetry / Drama   Pg. 129
Veinte poemas de amor y una canción desesperada   Poetry / Drama   Pg. 142
Libro de las preguntas   Children / Young Adults   Pg. 192

Nervo, Amado.
La amada inmóvil   Poetry / Drama   Pg. 123

Neuman, Andrés, ed.
Pequeñas resistencias: antología del nuevo cuento español   Literature / Fiction   Pg. 73

Nonídez García, Manuel.
En el nombre de los hombres   Children / Young Adults   Pg. 174

Novás Calvo, Lino.
Cayo Canas   Literature / Fiction   Pg. 30

Núñez Cabeza de Vaca, Alvar.
Naufragios y Comentarios   Non fiction   Pg. 112

O

Obiols, Anna.
Las aventuras de Don Quijote   Children / Young Adults   Pg. 190

Obregón, Baltasar.
Historia de los descubrimientos de Nueva España   Non fiction   Pg. 107

Ocampo, Silvina.
Cuentos completos   Literature / Fiction   Pg. 38

Olaizola Lazkano, Jesús Mari.
El tío Bin Floren   Children / Young Adults   Pg. 183

Olalla Linares, Carlos.
¿Quién mató a Regiomontano?   Children / Young Adults   Pg. 183

Olivares, Tina.
Au revoir, Marie   Children / Young Adults   Pg. 183

Ollero, Julio, and Susana Bardón, eds.
El mercado del libro antiguo español: una guía de precios   Reference   Pg. 154

Onetti, Juan Carlos.
El astillero   Literature / Fiction   Pg. 24

Orozco, Rebeca.
El Arca de Valores   Children / Young Adults   Pg. 164

Ortega y Gasset, José.
Misión del bibliotecario y otros ensayos afines   Non fiction   Pg. 111
La rebelión de las masas   Non fiction   Pg. 116

Ortiz, Fernando.
Contrapunto cubano del tabaco y azúcar   Non fiction   Pg. 102

P

Pacheco, José Emilio.
Las batallas del desierto   Literature / Fiction   Pg. 25

Padura, Leonardo.
Adiós Hemingway   Literature / Fiction   Pg. 20
Máscaras   Literature / Fiction   Pg. 61
La novela de mi vida   Literature / Fiction   Pg. 67

Palés Matos, Luis.
Tuntún de pasa y grifería   Poetry / Drama   Pg. 142

Pané, Ramón, Fray, and José Juan Arrom, ed.
Relación acerca de las antigüedades de los indios   Non fiction   Pg. 116

Paranaguá, Paulo Antonio.
Cine documental en América Latina   Reference   Pg. 145

Parra, Teresa de la.
Memorias de Mama Blanca   Literature / Fiction   Pg. 62

Paszkowski, Diego.
Tesis de un homicidio   Literature / Fiction   Pg. 87

Paz Soldán, Edmundo.
El delirio de Turing   Literature / Fiction   Pg. 39

Paz, Octavio.
El laberinto de la soledad   Literature / Fiction   Pg. 56
Traducción: literatura y literalidad   Non fiction   Pg. 117
Piedra de sol   Poetry / Drama   Pg. 136

Pereyra, Emilia.
Cenizas del querer   Literature / Fiction   Pg. 30

Pérez Galdós, Benito.
Fortunata y Jacinta: dos historias de casadas   Literature / Fiction   Pg. 45

Pérez Perucha, Julio, ed.
Antología crítica del cine español: 1906-1995   Reference   Pg. 145

Pérez - Reverte, Arturo.
El Club Dumas   Literature / Fiction   Pg. 33
El Asedio   Literature / Fiction   Pg. 23
La reina del sur   Literature / Fiction   Pg. 78

Peri Rossi, Cristina.
La última noche de Dostoievski   Literature / Fiction   Pg. 91

Piglia, Ricardo.
Plata quemada   Literature / Fiction   Pg. 74
Respiración artificial   Literature / Fiction   Pg. 79
Crítica y ficción   Non fiction   Pg. 102

Pinilla, Ramiro.
La higuera   Literature / Fiction   Pg. 49
Solo un muerto más   Literature / Fiction   Pg. 84

Pinto Martín, Sagrario.
Princesa va al teatro   Children / Young Adults   Pg. 170

Piñera, Virgilio.
La carne de René   Literature / Fiction   Pg. 28

Pitol, Sergio.
Los mejores cuentos   Literature / Fiction   Pg. 61

Pizarnik, Alejandra.
Obras completas: Poesía completa y prosa selecta   Poetry / Drama   Pg. 135

Pla, Josep.
El cuaderno gris   Non fiction   Pg. 105

Pla, Josefina.
Antología poética   Poetry / Drama   Pg. 124

Poniatowska, Elena.
Hasta no verte, Jesús mío   Literature / Fiction   Pg. 47
El tren pasa primero   Literature / Fiction   Pg. 89
La noche de Tlatelolco   Non fiction   Pg. 113

Pozas, Ricardo.
Juan Pérez Jolote: biografía de un tzotzil   Non fiction   Pg. 109

Prats Martínez,Lluís ; Roig Tió, Enric.
El laboratorio secreto   Children / Young Adults   Pg. 186

Preston, Paul.
Franco, Caudillo de España   Non fiction   Pg. 107

Puccini, Giacomo; Prats Pijoan, Joan de Déu.
Turandot   Children / Young Adults   Pg. 195

Puértolas, Soledad.
Historia de un abrigo   Literature / Fiction   Pg. 50

Puig, Manuel.
El beso de la mujer araña   Literature / Fiction   Pg. 26

Puig, Socorro, and María Stoopen.
Especialidades regionales de la cocina mexicana   Non fiction   Pg. 106

Puño.
Ñam   Children / Young Adults   Pg. 169

Quevedo, Francisco de.
Sueños y discursos   Literature / Fiction   Pg. 86
La vida del Buscón   Literature / Fiction   Pg. 92
Poesía varia   Poetry / Drama   Pg. 137

Quintero, Juan Carlos.
La caja negra   Poetry / Drama   Pg. 132

Quiroga, Horacio.
A la deriva y otros cuentos   Literature / Fiction   Pg. 19
Las medias de los flamencos   Children / Young Adults   Pg. 161

R

Ramírez, Sergio.
Margarita, está linda la mar   Literature / Fiction   Pg. 61

Ramírez Márquez, Alister.
Mi vestido verde esmeralda   Literature / Fiction   Pg. 63
Los sueños de los hombres se los fuman las mujeres   Literature / Fiction   Pg. 85
¿Quién se robó los colores?   Children / Young Adults   Pg. 181

Ramón Jiménez, Juan.
Platero y yo   Literature / Fiction   Pg. 74

Ramos, Jorge.
La ola Latina: cómo los hispanos están transformando la política en los Estados Unidos   Non fiction   Pg. 113

Ramos, Mario.
Soy el más guapo   Children / Young Adults   Pg. 170

Real Academia Española.
Diccionario de la lengua española   Reference   Pg. 147
Diccionario panhispánico de dudas   Reference   Pg. 149

Restrepo, Laura.
Delirio   Literature / Fiction   Pg. 40
La novia oscura   Literature / Fiction   Pg. 68

Reviejo Hernández, Carlos; Moreno Reborditos, Ana.
Abecedario de Arte   Children / Young Adults   Pg. 164

Reyes, Alfonso.
Visión de Anáhuac y otros ensayos   Non fiction   Pg. 119

Reyes, Edwin.
El arpa imaginaria   Poetry / Drama   Pg. 125

Ribeyro, Julio Ramón.
Antología personal   Literature / Fiction   Pg. 22

Rico, Francisco, ed.
Historia y crítica de la literatura española   Reference   Pg. 153

Ridruejo, Dionisio.
Cuadernos de Rusia   Non fiction   Pg. 103

Riera, Carmen.
En el último azul   Literature / Fiction Pg. 42

Ríos Avila, Rubén.
La Raza Cómica: Del sujeto en Puerto Rico   Non fiction   Pg. 116

Rivas, Manuel.
El lápiz del carpintero   Literature / Fiction Pg. 56
Los libros arden mal   Literature / Fiction Pg. 58

Rivera de Alvarez, Josefina.
Literatura Puertorriqueña: Su proceso en el tiempo   Reference   Pg. 153

Rivera Letelier, Hernán.
La reina Isabel cantaba rancheras   Literature / Fiction Pg. 78

Rivers, Elias L.
Renaissance and Baroque Poetry of Spain   Poetry / Drama   Pg. 139

Roa Bastos, Augusto.
Yo el supremo   Literature / Fiction Pg. 94

Roa Bastos, Augusto; Maciel, Alejandro.
Polisapo   Children / Young Adults Pg. 181

Rodgers, Eamonn, ed.
Encyclopedia of contemporary Spanish culture   Reference   Pg. 151

Rodoreda, Mercè.
La plaza del diamante   Literature / Fiction Pg. 75

Rodríguez Juliá, Edgardo.
El entierro de Cortijo   Literature / Fiction Pg. 43

Rodríguez, Antonio Orlando
Aprendices de brujo   Literature / Fiction Pg. 22
Chiquita   Literature / Fiction Pg. 31
La gata de los pintores   Children / Young Adults Pg. 167
La isla viajera   Children / Young Adults Pg. 168
El rock de la momia y otros versos diversos   Children / Young Adults Pg. 182

Rojas, Manuel.
Hijo de ladrón   Literature / Fiction Pg. 49

Rojas, Gonzalo.
¿Qué se ama cuando se ama?   Poetry / Drama   Pg. 139

Rojas, Fernando de.
La Celestina — Poetry / Drama — Pg. 132

Roldán, Gustavo.
Disparates — Children / Young Adults — Pg. 166

Rolón, Gabriel.
Palabras cruzadas — Non fiction — Pg. 114

Romeu, Emma.
Ahí viene el lobo gris — Non fiction — Pg. 97
Gregorio y el mar — Children / Young Adults — Pg. 175
Las patas del flamenco — Children / Young Adults — Pg. 180
El rey de las octavas — Children / Young Adults — Pg. 182

Roncagliolo, Santiago.
Abril Rojo — Literature / Fiction — Pg. 19
Pudor — Literature / Fiction — Pg. 76

Rondón, Javier.
El sapo distraído — Children / Young Adults — Pg. 163

Rubio, Antonio; and Villán, Oscar.
Luna — Children / Young Adults — Pg. 168

Ruiz de Alarcón, Juan.
La verdad sospechosa — Literature / Fiction — Pg. 94

Ruiz Zafón, Carlos.
El Juego del Angel — Literature / Fiction — Pg. 54
La sombra del viento — Literature / Fiction — Pg. 85
El príncipe de la niebla — Children / Young Adults — Pg. 194

Rulfo, Juan.
Pedro Páramo — Literature / Fiction — Pg. 73

S

Sábato, Ernesto.
El túnel — Literature / Fiction — Pg. 90

Saer, Juan José.
El entenado — Literature / Fiction — Pg. 42

Sáez Castán, Javier.
La merienda del señor Verde — Children / Young Adults — Pg. 179

Sales, Joan.
Incierta gloria — Literature / Fiction — Pg. 52

Salinas, Jaime.
Travesías   Non fiction   Pg. 118

Sánchez Ferlosio, Rafael.
Industrias y andanzas de Alfanhuí   Literature / Fiction   Pg. 53

Sánchez Piñol, Albert.
La piel fría   Literature / Fiction   Pg. 55

Sánchez, Luis Rafael.
La guaracha del Macho Camacho   Literature / Fiction   Pg. 46

Santiago, Esmeralda.
Cuando era puertorriqueña   Non fiction   Pg. 103

Santis, Pablo de.
El inventor de juegos   Children / Young Adults   Pg. 186

Santos Torres, Care.
Maddox descubre el camino   Children / Young Adults   Pg. 178

Saramago, José.
Caín   Literature / Fiction   Pg. 28

Sarmiento de Gamboa, Pedro.
Viajes al estrecho de Magallanes   Non fiction   Pg. 119

Satrapi, Marjane.
Persépolis   Literature / Fiction   Pg. 74

Seco, Manuel.
Diccionario de dudas y dificultades de la lengua española   Reference   Pg. 146
Diccionario fraseológico documentado del español actual: locuciones y modismos   Reference   Pg. 149

Segura Soler, Gabriel.
Ya está aquí ¡Don invierno!   Children / Young Adults   Pg. 184

Semprún, Jorge.
El largo viaje   Non fiction   Pg. 109

Sención, Viriato.
Los que falsificaron la firma de Dios   Literature / Fiction   Pg. 76

Sender, Ramón J.
Imán   Literature / Fiction   Pg. 52
Réquiem por un campesino español   Literature / Fiction   Pg. 79

Seoane, María.
La noche de los lápices   Non fiction   Pg. 113

Sepúlveda, Luis.
Historia de una gaviota y del gato que le enseñó a volar   Literature / Fiction   Pg. 50
Nombre de torero   Literature / Fiction   Pg. 67
La sombra de lo que fuimos   Literature / Fiction   Pg. 84

Serrano, Marcela.
Lo que está en mi corazón   Literature / Fiction   Pg. 58

Silva, Lorenzo.
El alquimista impaciente   Literature / Fiction   Pg. 21

Sinán, Rogelio.
Plenilunio   Literature / Fiction   Pg. 75

Skármeta, Antonio.
El cartero de Neruda: ardiente paciencia   Literature / Fiction   Pg. 29
No pasó nada   Literature / Fiction   Pg. 67

Skirius, John ed.
El ensayo hispanoamericano del siglo XX   Non fiction   Pg. 105

Sobrino, Javier.
Me Gusta   Children / Young Adults   Pg. 161

Soler, Jordi.
Los rojos de ultramar   Literature / Fiction   Pg. 80

Soriano, Osvaldo.
Triste, solitario y final   Literature / Fiction   Pg. 90

Stavans, Ilan, editor in chief, and Harold Augenbraum, associate editor.
Encyclopedia Latina: History, Culture and Society in the United States   Reference   Pg. 150

Suances Torres, Jaime.
Diccionario del verbo español, hispanoamericano y dialectal   Reference   Pg. 148

T

Taboada Terán, Néstor.
Indios en rebelión   Literature / Fiction   Pg. 52

Taibo II, Paco.
Algunas nubes   Literature / Fiction   Pg. 20

Teixidor, Emili.
La hormiga Miga... ¡liga!   Children / Young Adults   Pg. 176

Tenembaum, Barbara A., and Georgette M. Dorn, eds.
Encyclopedia of Latin American history and culture   Reference   Pg. 151

Toro Sugrañés, José A.
Nueva Enciclopedia de Puerto Rico — Reference — Pg. 154

Torrente Ballester, Gonzalo.
La saga/fuga de J.B. — Literature / Fiction — Pg. 81

Torres, Victor F.
Diccionario de autores puertorriqueños contemporáneos — Reference — Pg. 146

U

Unamuno, Miguel de.
Niebla — Literature / Fiction — Pg. 66
San Manuel Bueno Mártir — Literature / Fiction — Pg. 81
Del sentimiento trágico de la vida — Non fiction — Pg. 104

Urberuaga, Emilio.
Coco y la Luna — Children / Young Adults — Pg. 159

Uribe, Alvaro y Sears, Olivia.
Best of Contemporary Mexican Fiction — Literature / Fiction — Pg. 26

Uribe, María de la Luz.
Historia del uno — Children / Young Adults — Pg. 160

Usigli, Rodolfo.
Corona de sombra — Literature / Fiction — Pg. 35
Ensayo de un crimen — Literature / Fiction — Pg. 42

V W

Valdecasas, Blanca.
Por donde sale el sol — Literature / Fiction — Pg. 75

Valdés, Zoe.
Te di la vida entera — Literature / Fiction — Pg. 86
Café nostalgia — Literature / Fiction — Pg. 28
La nada cotidiana — Literature / Fiction — Pg. 66

Valdez Cardenas, Javier.
Miss Narco — Non fiction — Pg. 111

Valente, José Ángel.
No amanece el cantor — Poetry / Drama — Pg. 133

Valle, Ignacio del.
El tiempo de los emperadores extraños — Literature / Fiction — Pg. 88

Valle, Antonio.
Tino y la alfombra mágica — Children / Young Adults — Pg. 171

Valle Inclán, Ramón María del.
Luces de bohemia — Poetry / Drama — Pg. 133

Vallejo, César.
Trilce — Poetry / Drama — Pg. 142

Vargas Llosa, Mario.
La ciudad y los perros — Literature / Fiction — Pg. 33
Conversación en la Catedral — Literature / Fiction — Pg. 34
La fiesta del Chivo — Literature / Fiction — Pg. 45
El hablador — Literature / Fiction — Pg. 47
Pantaleón y las visitadoras — Literature / Fiction — Pg. 71
La tía Julia y el escribidor — Literature / Fiction — Pg. 87
Travesuras de la niña mala — Literature / Fiction — Pg. 88
El pez en en el agua: memorias — Non fiction — Pg. 105

Various.
Por el libro — Literature / Fiction — Pg. 76
Historias de Verdad — Non fiction — Pg. 108

Vázquez Montalbán, Manuel.
Asesinato en el comité central — Literature / Fiction — Pg. 23
Galíndez — Literature / Fiction — Pg. 46

Vázquez, Lourdes.
Sin ti no soy yo — Literature / Fiction — Pg. 83

Vázquez, Ángel.
La vida perra de Juanita Narboni — Literature / Fiction — Pg. 93

Veerbitsky, Horacio.
El silencio — Non fiction — Pg. 117

Vega, Garcilaso de la.
Comentarios Reales — Non fiction — Pg. 101
Poesías castellanas completas — Poetry / Drama — Pg. 138
La Florida del Inca — Non fiction — Pg. 107

Vega, Lope de.
Fuenteovejuna — Poetry / Drama — Pg. 131
Poesías liricas — Poetry / Drama — Pg. 138

Velásquez Guzmán, Mónica, ed.
Antología de la poesía boliviana: ordenar la danza — Poetry / Drama — Pg. 123

Veloz Maggiolo, Marcio.
Materia Prima: Protonovela — Literature / Fiction — Pg. 61

Ventosilla, Walter.
A quien corresponda   Literature / Fiction   Pg. 19
Cuentos de tierra y eucaliptos   Literature / Fiction   Pg. 38
Luis bandolero Luis   Literature / Fiction   Pg. 59

Vergés, Pedro.
Sólo cenizas hallarás (bolero)   Literature / Fiction   Pg. 84

Vicent, Manuel.
Son de Mar   Literature / Fiction   Pg. 85

Vidal, César.
Diccionario del Quijote:
la obra para entender uno de los libros esenciales de la cultura universal   Reference   Pg. 148

Vila Matas, Enrique.
Hijos sin hijos   Literature / Fiction   Pg. 50

Villoro, Juan.
El testigo   Literature / Fiction   Pg. 87

Villota Rocha, José Andrés.
Leo el dragón lector   Children / Young Adults   Pg. 168

Volpi, Jorge.
En busca de Klingsor   Literature / Fiction   Pg. 41
No será la tierra   Literature / Fiction   Pg. 67
Oscuro Bosque Oscuro   Literature / Fiction   Pg. 71

Walsh, Rodolfo.
Operación Masacre   Literature / Fiction   Pg. 70

XYZ

Zeno Gandía, Manuel.
La charca   Literature / Fiction   Pg. 31

Zubizarreta, Patxi.
Tres amigos   Children / Young Adults   Pg. 183
Enciclopedia Hispánica   Reference   Pg. 150

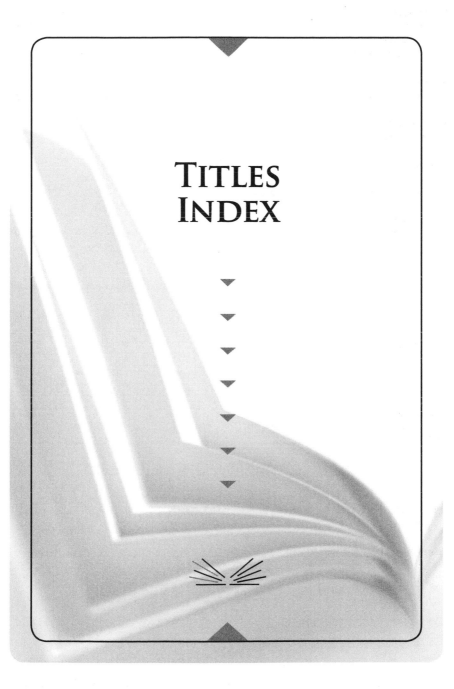

TITLES
INDEX

#

100 Cartas Personales / Juan Sebastián González.	Reference	Pg. 145
Los 1001 años de la lengua española / Antonio Alatorre.	Non fiction	Pg. 97
25 cuentos tradicionales españoles / Edición de José María Guelbenzu.	Children / Young Adults	Pg. 173
2666 / Roberto Bolaño.	Literature / Fiction	Pg. 19

A

A la deriva y otros cuentos / Horacio Quiroga.	Literature / Fiction	Pg. 19
A la Tierra le ha salido una gotera / Agatha Echevarría Canales.	Children / Young Adults	Pg. 164
A quien corresponda / Walter Ventosilla.	Literature / Fiction	Pg. 19
A una nariz pegado / Juan Kruz Igerabide Sarasola.	Children / Young Adults	Pg. 173
Abecedario de Arte / Carlos Reviejo Hernández; Ana Moreno Reborditos.	Children / Young Adults	Pg. 164
Abril Rojo / Santiago Roncagliolo.	Literature / Fiction	Pg. 19
Adiós Hemingway / Leonardo Padura.	Literature / Fiction	Pg. 20
Adire y el tiempo roto / Manuel Granados.	Literature / Fiction	Pg. 20
Ahí viene el lobo gris / Emma Romeu.	Non fiction	Pg. 97
El Aleph / Jorge Luis Borges.	Literature / Fiction	Pg. 20
Algunas nubes / Paco Taibo II.	Literature / Fiction	Pg. 20
El alma del bosque / Manuel López Gallego.	Children / Young Adults	Pg. 189
El alquimista impaciente / Lorenzo Silva.	Literature / Fiction	Pg. 21
Altazor o el viaje en paracaídas / Vicente Huidobro.	Poetry / Drama	Pg. 123
La amada inmóvil / Amado Nervo	Poetry / Drama	Pg. 123
La amigdalitis de Tarzán / Alfredo Bryce Echenique.	Literature / Fiction	Pg. 55
El amor en los tiempos del cólera / Gabriel García Márquez.	Literature / Fiction	Pg. 21
El amor, las mujeres y la vida / Mario Benedetti.	Children / Young Adults	Pg. 189
La amortajada / María Luisa Bombal.	Literature / Fiction	Pg. 21
Animal de fondo / Juan Ramón Jiménez.	Poetry / Drama	Pg. 123
Animales... son muchos y no son iguales / María Lucía Carvalhas.	Children / Young Adults	Pg. 159
Antes que anochezca: autobiografía / Reinaldo Arenas.	Literature / Fiction	Pg. 21
Antología crítica del cine español: 1906-1995 / Julio Pérez Perucha, ed.	Reference	Pg. 145
Antología de la poesía boliviana: ordenar la danza / Mónica Velásquez Guzmán, ed.	Poetry / Drama	Pg. 123
Antología del grupo poético de 1927 / Vicente Gaos, ed.	Poetry / Drama	Pg. 124
Antología personal / Julio Ramón Ribeyro.	Literature / Fiction	Pg. 22
Antología personal / José Agustín Goytisolo.	Poetry / Drama	Pg. 124
Antología poética / Federico García Lorca.	Poetry / Drama	Pg. 124
Antología poética / Josefina Pla.	Poetry / Drama	Pg. 125
Antología poética / Antonio Machado.	Poetry / Drama	Pg. 125
Aprendamos Español. Diccionario Ilustrado / Marlene Goodman.	Children / Young Adults	Pg. 189
Aprendices de brujo / Antonio Orlando Rodríguez.	Literature / Fiction	Pg.22

La Araucana / Alonso de Ercilla. ..... Non fiction ..... Pg. 97

El árbol de la ciencia / Pío Baroja. ..... Literature / Fiction ..... Pg. 22

El Arca de Valores / Rebeca Orozco. ..... Children / Young Adults ..... Pg. 164

Los Argonautas / Apollonius of Rhodes; Rafael Ballester Escalas. ..... Children / Young Adults ..... Pg. 190

El argumento de la obra: correspondencia (1951-1989) / Jaime Gil de Biedma ..... Non fiction ..... Pg. 97

El arpa imaginaria / Edwin Reyes. ..... Poetry / Drama ..... Pg. 125

Arráncame la vida / Angeles Mastretta. ..... Literature / Fiction ..... Pg. 22

Artículos / Mariano José de Larra. ..... Non fiction ..... Pg. 98

El Asco: Thomas Bernhard en El Salvador / Horacio Castellanos Moya. ..... Literature / Fiction ..... Pg. 23

El Asedio / Arturo Pérez-Reverte. ..... Literature / Fiction ..... Pg. 23

Asesinato en el comité central / Manuel Vázquez Montalbán. ..... Literature / Fiction ..... Pg. 23

El astillero / Juan Carlos Onetti. ..... Literature / Fiction ..... Pg. 24

Atletas de las Tierras Altas / Nacho Docavo Alberti. ..... Children / Young Adults ..... Pg. 185

Au revoir, Marie / Tina Olivares. ..... Children / Young Adults ..... Pg. 185

Las aventuras de Don Quijote / Anna Obiols. ..... Children / Young Adults ..... Pg. 190

Aventuras literarias / Ana C. Jarvis, Raquel Lebredo, and Francisco Mena Ayllón. ..... Literature / Fiction ..... Pg. 24

Aves sin nido / Clorinda Matto de Turner. ..... Literature / Fiction ..... Pg. 24

El azul de la tierra / Eugenio Montejo. ..... Poetry / Drama ..... Pg. 126

Azul / Rubén Darío. ..... Poetry / Drama ..... Pg. 125

Azul; España contemporánea; Cantos de vida y esperanza / Rubén Darío. ..... Poetry / Drama ..... Pg. 126

B

Balas de plata / Elmer Mendoza. ..... Literature / Fiction ..... Pg. 24

Balún Canán / Rosario Castellanos. ..... Literature / Fiction ..... Pg. 25

Barrio de maravillas / Rosa Chacel. ..... Literature / Fiction ..... Pg. 25

Las batallas del desierto / José Emilio Pacheco. ..... Literature / Fiction ..... Pg. 25

Bendíceme, Última / Rudolfo Anaya. ..... Literature / Fiction ..... Pg. 25

El beso de la mujer araña / Manuel Puig. ..... Literature / Fiction ..... Pg. 26

Best of Contemporary Mexican Fiction / Alvaro Uribe y Olivia Sears. ..... Literature / Fiction ..... Pg. 26

Bestiario / Juan José Arreola. ..... Literature / Fiction ..... Pg. 26

La Bien Plantada / Eugeni d'Ors. ..... Non fiction ..... Pg. 98

Biografía de un cimarrón / Miguel Barnet. ..... Non fiction ..... Pg. 98

El blues de la semana más negra / Andreu Martín Farrero. ..... Children / Young Adults ..... Pg. 190

Bodas de sangre / Federico García Lorca. ..... Poetry / Drama ..... Pg. 126

Bolinga / Elvira Lindo. ..... Children / Young Adults ..... Pg. 164

Bomarzo / Manuel Mujica Lainez. ..... Literature / Fiction ..... Pg. 26

Borges profesor: curso de Literatura inglesa en la U.B.A. / Martín Arias. ..... Non fiction ..... Pg. 99

Breve historia de la literatura española / Carlos Alvar, José Carlos Mainer, and Rosa Navarro. ..... Non fiction ..... Pg. 99

Brevísima relación de la destrucción de las Indias / Bartolomé de las Casas. ..... Non fiction ..... Pg. 99

Buenas noches a todos / Sergio Gómez. ..... Literature / Fiction ..... Pg. 27

El burlador de Sevilla / Tirso de Molina. ..... Poetry / Drama ..... Pg. 126

Buscando un Inca: identidad y utopía en los Andes / Alberto Flores Galindo.   Non fiction   Pg. 99

El caballo cobarde / Felipe Benítez Pérez.	Children / Young Adults	Pg. 173
Caballo de Troya / J.J. Benítez.	Literature / Fiction	Pg. 27
Café Hugo / Adolfo García Ortega.	Literature / Fiction	Pg. 27
Café nostalgia / Zoe Valdés.	Literature / Fiction	Pg. 28
Caín / José Saramago.	Literature / Fiction	Pg. 28
La caja negra / Juan Carlos Quintero.	Poetry / Drama	Pg. 132
Campos de Castilla / Antonio Machado.	Poetry / Drama	Pg. 127
Campos de Níjar / Juan Goytisolo.	Non fiction	Pg. 100
Cancionero popular mexicano / Mario Kuri Aldana, and Vicente Mendoza Martínez.	Non fiction	Pg. 100
Cancionero y romancero de ausencias / Miguel Hernández.	Poetry / Drama	Pg. 127
Cantar de Mío Cid / Anonymous	Poetry / Drama	Pg. 127
Cantigas de Santa María / Alfonso X el Sabio.	Poetry / Drama	Pg. 128
Canto general / Pablo Neruda	Poetry / Drama	Pg. 128
Cantos de vida y esperanza / Rubén Darío.	Poetry / Drama	Pg. 128
Caramelo: puro cuento / Sandra Cisneros.	Literature / Fiction	Pg. 28
Carmina, la pingüina que viene de Argentina / Pep Castellano; Canto Nieto.	Children / Young Adults	Pg. 165
La carne de René / Virgilio Piñera.	Literature / Fiction	Pg. 28
Cartas de relación (1519-1526) / Hernán Cortés.	Non fiction	Pg. 100
El cartero de Neruda: ardiente paciencia / Antonio Skármeta.	Literature / Fiction	Pg. 29
Cartucho: relatos de la lucha en el norte de México / Nellie Campobello	Literature / Fiction	Pg. 29
La casa de Bernarda Alba / Federico García Lorca.	Poetry / Drama	Pg. 128
La casa de la laguna / Rosario Ferré.	Literature / Fiction	Pg. 29
La casa de los espíritus / Isabel Allende.	Literature / Fiction	Pg. 29
El castillo interior o las moradas / Santa Teresa de Jesús.	Poetry / Drama	Pg. 129
La catedral del mar / Ildefonso Falcones.	Literature / Fiction	Pg. 30
Cayo Canas / Lino Novás Calvo.	Literature / Fiction	Pg. 30
La Celestina / Fernando de Rojas.	Poetry / Drama	Pg. 132
Cenizas del querer / Emilia Pereyra.	Literature / Fiction	Pg. 30
Los centroamericanos: antología de cuentos / José Mejía, ed.	Literature / Fiction	Pg. 30
La charca / Manuel Zeno Gandía.	Literature / Fiction	Pg. 31
El chico de oro / Michael Nava.	Literature / Fiction	Pg. 31
Chiquita / Antonio Orlando Rodríguez.	Literature / Fiction	Pg. 31
Ciclo mágico de las estaciones / Francisco Alarcón.	Poetry / Drama	Pg. 129
El cielo a tu alcance / Michèle Mira Pons.	Children / Young Adults	Pg. 173
Cien años de soledad / Gabriel García Márquez.	Literature / Fiction	Pg. 31
Cien sonetos de amor / Pablo Neruda.	Poetry / Drama	Pg. 129
Cinco horas con Mario / Miguel Delibes.	Literature / Fiction	Pg. 32
Cinco maestros: Cuentos modernos de Hispanoamérica / Alexander Coleman.	Literature / Fiction	Pg. 32

Cine argentino / Claudio España, ed.	Reference	Pg. 145
Cine documental en América Latina / Paulo Antonio Paranaguá.	Reference	Pg. 145
Los cipreses creen en Dios / José María Gironella.	Literature / Fiction	Pg. 32
La ciudad de los prodigios / Eduardo Mendoza.	Literature / Fiction	Pg. 32
La ciudad y los perros / Mario Vargas Llosa.	Literature / Fiction	Pg. 33
El Club Dumas / Arturo Pérez-Reverte.	Literature / Fiction	Pg. 33
Coco y la Luna / Emilio Urberuaga.	Children / Young Adults	Pg.159
La colmena / Camilo José Cela.	Literature / Fiction	Pg. 33
El color del verano / Reinaldo Arenas.	Literature / Fiction	Pg. 33
Comentario de la Isagogé de Porfirio / Averroes.	Non fiction	Pg. 101
Comentarios Reales / Garcilaso de la Vega, Inca.	Non fiction	Pg. 101
Como agua para chocolate / Laura Esquivel.	Literature / Fiction	Pg. 34
Cómo leer y escribir poesía / Hugo Hiriart.	Non fiction	Pg. 101
Con los dedos de una mano / Isidro Ferrer Soria.	Children / Young Adults	Pg. 165
Condenados de Condado / Norberto Fuentes.	Literature / Fiction	Pg. 34
Confieso que he vivido / Pablo Neruda.	Non fiction	Pg. 102
Conspiración Maine / Mario Escobar Golderos.	Literature / Fiction	Pg. 34
Contrapunto cubano del tabaco y azúcar / Fernando Ortiz.	Non fiction	Pg. 102
Contrapunto de género y raza en Puerto Rico / Idsa E. Alegría Ortega, and Palmira N. Ríos, eds.	Non fiction	Pg. 102
Conversación en la Catedral / Mario Vargas Llosa.	Literature / Fiction	Pg. 34
Conversación entre escritoras del Caribe Hispano: Tomo II / Daisy Cocco De Filippis, and Sonia Rivera Valdéz, eds.	Non fiction	Pg. 102
Copérnico / Carlos Blanco.	Children / Young Adults	Pg. 191
El corazón del tártaro / Rosa Montero.	Literature / Fiction	Pg. 35
Corazón tan blanco / Javier Marías.	Literature / Fiction	Pg. 35
Corona de sombra / Rodolfo Usigli.	Literature / Fiction	Pg. 35
El coronel no tiene quien le escriba / Gabriel García Márquez.	Literature / Fiction	Pg. 35
Cortos / Alberto Fuguet.	Literature / Fiction	Pg. 36
Cristo versus Arizona / Camilo José Cela.	Literature / Fiction	Pg. 36
Crítica y ficción / Ricardo Piglia.	Non fiction	Pg. 102
Crónica sentimental en rojo / Francisco González Ledesma.	Literature / Fiction	Pg. 36
La Cruz del Diablo / Carlos Adolfo Bécquer.	Children / Young Adults	Pg. 191
Cruzando la frontera: la crónica implacable de una familia mexicana que emigra a Estados Unidos / Rubén Martínez.	Non fiction	Pg. 103
Cuaderno de Nueva York / José Hierro.	Poetry / Drama	Pg. 129
El cuaderno gris / Josep Pla.	Non fiction	Pg. 105
Cuadernos de Rusia / Dionisio Ridruejo.	Non fiction	Pg. 103
Cuando era puertorriqueña / Esmeralda Santiago.	Non fiction	Pg. 103
El cuarto de atrás / Carmen Martín Gaite.	Literature / Fiction	Pg. 37
La Cucaracha Martina: un cuento folklórico del Caribe / Daniel Moreton.	Children / Young Adults	Pg. 159
El cuento hispánico: A graded Literary Anthology / Edward J. Mullen, and John F. Garganigo.	Literature / Fiction	Pg. 37
Cuentos completos (1968-2002) / José Agustín.	Literature / Fiction	Pg. 37
Cuentos completos / Julio Cortázar.	Literature / Fiction	Pg. 37

Cuentos completos / Silvina Ocampo.	Literature / Fiction	Pg. 38
Cuentos de Culver City / José Luis Borau.	Literature / Fiction	Pg. 38
Cuentos de tierra y eucaliptos / Walter Ventosilla.	Literature / Fiction	Pg. 38
Cuentos del gallo de oro / Juan Pedro Aparicio, Luis Mateo Diez, José María Merino.	Literature / Fiction	Pg. 39
Cúper, perro volador / Montse Ganges.	Children / Young Adults	Pg. 159
Curso de redacción. Teoría y práctica de la composición y del estilo / Gonzalo Martín Vivaldi.	Non fiction	Pg. 103

D

La dama del alba / Alejandro Casona.	Literature / Fiction	Pg. 39
El dardo en la palabra / Fernando Lázaro Carreter.	Non fiction	Pg. 104
Los de abajo / Mariano Azuela.	Literature / Fiction	Pg. 59
De Cristóbal Colón a Fidel Castro. El Caribe, frontera imperial / Juan Bosch.	Non fiction	Pg. 104
El decir y el vértigo: Panorama de la poesía hispanoamericana reciente (1963-1979) / Rocío Cerón, Julián Herbert, and León Plascencia Ñol.	Poetry / Drama	Pg. 130
Del amor y otros demonios / Gabriel García Márquez.	Literature / Fiction	Pg. 39
Del lado del amor / Juan Antonio González Iglesias.	Poetry / Drama	Pg. 130
Del Ombligo de la Luna / Francisco Alarcón; illustrator: Maya Maribel Suárez.	Children / Young Adults	Pg. 171
Del sentimiento trágico de la vida / Miguel de Unamuno.	Non fiction	Pg. 104
El delirio de Turing / Edmundo Paz Soldán.	Literature / Fiction	Pg. 39
Delirio / Laura Restrepo.	Literature / Fiction	Pg. 40
Los detectives salvajes / Roberto Bolaño.	Literature / Fiction	Pg. 40
El diario azul de Carlota / Gemma Lienas Massot.	Children / Young Adults	Pg. 191
Diario de Argónida / José Manuel Caballero Bonald.	Poetry / Drama	Pg. 130
Días contados / Juan Madrid.	Literature / Fiction	Pg. 40
Diccionario crítico etimológico castellano e hispánico / Joan Corominas.	Reference	Pg. 146
Diccionario de autores latinoamericanos / César Aira.	Reference	Pg. 146
Diccionario de autores puertorriqueños contemporáneos / Victor F. Torres	Reference	Pg. 146
Diccionario de dudas y dificultades de la lengua española / Manuel Seco.	Reference	Pg. 146
Diccionario de escritores en lengua castellana: quién es quién hoy en las letras españolas / Twiggy Hirota, ed.	Reference	Pg. 147
Diccionario de la lengua española / Real Academia Española.	Reference	Pg. 147
Diccionario de la literatura española e hispanoamericana / Ricardo Gullón, dir.	Reference	Pg. 147
Diccionario de la música española e hispanoamericana / Emilio Casares Rodicio, dir. y coord. general, José López Calo, dir., and Ismael Fernández de la Cuesta, dir.	Reference	Pg. 147
Diccionario del cine español / José Luis Borau, ed.	Reference	Pg. 148
Diccionario del Quijote: la obra para entender uno de los libros esenciales de la cultura universal / César Vidal.	Reference	Pg. 148
Diccionario del uso del español / María Moliner.	Reference	Pg. 148
Diccionario del verbo español, hispanoamericano y dialectal / Jaime Suances Torres.	Reference	Pg. 148
Diccionario fraseológico documentado del español actual: locuciones y modismos / Manuel Seco.	Reference	Pg. 149

Diccionario ideológico de la lengua española / Julio Casares.	Reference	Pg. 149
Diccionario panhispánico de dudas / Real Academia Española.	Reference	Pg. 149
Discurso del oso / Julio Cortázar.	Children / Young Adults	Pg. 165
Disparates / Gustavo Roldán.	Children / Young Adults	Pg. 166
Distinguida Señora / Carmen Imbert Brugal.	Literature / Fiction	Pg. 40
Doce preguntas a un piano / Juan Cruz Igerabide Sarasola.	Children / Young Adults	Pg. 185
Don Quijote de la Mancha / Miguel de Cervantes.	Literature / Fiction	Pg. 41
Doña Bárbara / Rómulo Gallegos.	Literature / Fiction	Pg. 41
Doña Flautina Resuelvelotodo / Yanitzia Canetti; Avi.	Children / Young Adults	Pg. 166
Dos crímenes / Jorge Ibargüengoitia.	Literature / Fiction	Pg. 41

E

En busca de Klingsor / Jorge Volpi.	Literature / Fiction	Pg. 41
En busca del unicornio / Juan Eslava Galán.	Literature / Fiction	Pg. 27
En el nombre de los hombres / Manuel Nonídez García.	Children / Young Adults	Pg. 174
En el último azul / Carmen Riera.	Literature / Fiction	Pg. 42
En qué creen los que no creen / Umberto Eco.	Poetry / Drama	Pg. 131
En tiempos difíciles / Yanitzia Canetti; Romont Willy	Children / Young Adults	Pg. 166
Enciclopedia de la novela española / Rafael del Moral.	Reference	Pg. 150
Enciclopedia Hispánica.	Reference	Pg. 150
Encyclopedia Latina: History, Culture and Society in the United States / Ilan Stavans, editor in chief, and Harold Augenbraum, associate editor.	Reference	Pg. 150
Encyclopedia of contemporary Latin American and Caribbean cultures / Daniel Balderston, Mike González, and Ana M. López, eds.	Reference	Pg. 150
Encyclopedia of contemporary Spanish culture / Eamonn Rodgers, ed.	Reference	Pg. 151
Encyclopedia of Latin American history and culture / Barbara A. Tenembaum, and Georgette M. Dorn, eds.	Reference	Pg. 151
Ensayo de un crimen / Rodolfo Usigli.	Literature / Fiction	Pg. 42
El ensayo hispanoamericano del siglo XX / John Skirius, ed.	Non fiction	Pg. 105
La enseñanza del gran río / Mercedes Beatriz Wurm.	Children / Young Adults	Pg. 185
Enseñar a traducir: metodología en la formación de traductores e intérpretes / Amparo Hurtado Albir.	Non fiction	Pg. 105
El entenado / Juan José Saer.	Literature / Fiction	Pg. 42
El entierro de Cortijo / Edgardo Rodríguez Juliá.	Literature / Fiction	Pg. 43
La esclavitud del negro en Santo Domingo / Carlos Esteban Deive.	Non fiction	Pg. 106
Escrituras de Frida Kahlo / Frida Kahlo.	Non fiction	Pg. 106
Escucha mis manos / Alvarito Cuevas.	Children / Young Adults	Pg. 174
Escuela de mandarines / Miguel Espinosa.	Literature / Fiction	Pg. 43
España en su historia / Américo Castro.	Non fiction	Pg. 106
Especialidades regionales de la cocina mexicana / Socorro Puig & María Stoopen	Non fiction	Pg. 106
El estadio de mármol / Juan Bonilla.	Literature / Fiction	Pg. 43

Eva Luna / Isabel Allende.   Literature / Fiction   Pg. 43

F

Fábulas de una abuela extraterrestre / Daína Chaviano.   Literature / Fiction   Pg. 44
La familia de Pascual Duarte / Camilo José Cela.   Literature / Fiction   Pg. 44
Farabeuf / Salvador Elizondo.   Literature / Fiction   Pg. 44
Federico / Leo Arias.   Children / Young Adults   Pg. 160
Federico García Lorca / Georgina Lázaro.   Children / Young Adults   Pg. 174
Federico García Lorca para niños y niñas... y otros seres curiosos / Federico García Lorca.   Children / Young Adults   Pg. 175
Federico García Lorca / Ian Gibson.   Non fiction   Pg. 106
Ficciones / Jorge Luis Borges.   Literature / Fiction   Pg. 45
La fiesta del Chivo / Mario Vargas Llosa.   Literature / Fiction   Pg. 45
El flamboyán amarillo / Georgina Lázaro.   Children / Young Adults   Pg. 166
Las flores de nieve y el zorrito / Africa Coll Fernández.   Children / Young Adults   Pg. 167
La Florida del Inca / Garcilaso de la Vega.   Non fiction   Pg. 107
La forja de un rebelde / Arturo Barea.   Literature / Fiction   Pg. 45
Fortunata y Jacinta: dos historias de casadas / Benito Pérez Galdós. Literature / Fiction   Pg. 45
Franco, Caudillo de España / Paul Preston.   Non fiction   Pg. 107
Fuenteovejuna / Lope de Vega.   Poetry / Drama   Pg. 131

G

Gabirochi y la isla de la vida / RR Gruerra.   Children / Young Adults   Pg. 175
Galíndez / Manuel Vázquez Montalbán.   Literature / Fiction   Pg. 46
Gálvez y el cambio del cambio / Jorge Martínez Reverte.   Literature / Fiction   Pg. 46
Gasol por Pau Gasol. El partido de mi vida /
Pau Gasol Sáez; Jesús Sáez; Fernando Carreño Ocaña.   Children / Young Adults   Pg. 186
Gastronomía saludable / Rafael Ansón & Gregorio Varela.   Non fiction   Pg. 107
La gata de los pintores / Antonio Orlando Rodríguez.   Children / Young Adults   Pg. 167
Generación del 27. Poemas / José Antonio García.   Children / Young Adults   Pg. 192
Los girasoles ciegos / Alberto Méndez.   Literature / Fiction   Pg. 46
Gracias / Thanks / Pat Mora; illustrator: John Parra.   Children / Young Adults   Pg. 167
Gramática de la lengua castellana dedicada al uso de los americanos / Andrés Bello.   Reference   Pg. 151
Gramática descriptiva de la lengua española / Ignacio dir. Bosque, and Violeta Demonte, dir.   Reference   Pg. 151
**Gran diccionario Oxford: español-inglés, inglés-español = The Oxford Spanish Dictionary:
Spanish-English, English-Spanish** / Beatriz Galimberti Jarman, and Roy Russell.   Reference   Pg. 152
El Gran Guerrero / Pello Añorga.   Children / Young Adults   Pg. 175
La gran montaña / José Antonio Delgado.   Children / Young Adults   Pg. 160
Gregorio y el mar / Emma Romeu.   Children / Young Adults   Pg. 175
La guaracha del Macho Camacho / Luis Rafael Sánchez.   Literature / Fiction   Pg. 46

La Guía de Salud: Consejos y respuestas para la mujer latina / Jane Delgado   Non fiction   Pg. 107
Guzmán de Alfarache / Mateo Alemán.   Literature / Fiction   Pg. 47

H

El hablador / Mario Vargas Llosa.   Literature / Fiction   Pg. 47
El hada Oriana. El árbol. El espejo / Sophia de Mello Breyner Andresen.   Children / Young Adults   Pg. 176
Hasta el fin de los cuentos / José María Conget.   Literature / Fiction   Pg. 47
Hasta no verte, Jesús mío / Elena Poniatowska.   Literature / Fiction   Pg. 47
Hechos, dichos, occurrencias y andanzas de Bardín el Superrealista / Max.   Literature / Fiction   Pg. 48
Helena o el mar del verano / Julián Ayesta.   Literature / Fiction   Pg. 48
Los herederos de la fuerza / María Alamitos.   Children / Young Adults   Pg. 192
Herencia: The Anthology of Hispanic Literature of the United States / Nicolas Kanellos, ed.   Literature / Fiction   Pg. 48
Hermana muerte / Justo Navarro.   Literature / Fiction   Pg. 48
Herrumbrosas lanzas / Juan Benet.   Literature / Fiction   Pg. 49
Hijo de ladrón / Manuel Rojas.   Literature / Fiction   Pg. 49
El hijo del Buzo / Fernando Lalana Josa.   Children / Young Adults   Pg. 176
Hijos sin hijos / Enrique Vila Matas.   Literature / Fiction   Pg. 50
Hipotermia / Alvaro Enrigue.   Literature / Fiction   Pg. 50
Historia de la literatura española / Juan Luis Alborg.   Reference   Pg. 152
Historia de las mujeres en España y América Latina / Isabel Morant, dir.   Reference   Pg. 152
Historia de los descubrimientos de Nueva España / Baltasar Obregón.   Non fiction   Pg. 107
Historia de los indios de la Nueva España (1541) / Fray Toribio de Benavente, Motolinia.   Non fiction   Pg. 108
Historia de un abrigo / Soledad Puértolas.   Literature / Fiction   Pg. 50
Historia de una gaviota y del gato que le enseñó a volar / Luis Sepúlveda.   Literature / Fiction   Pg. 50
La historia del Rainbow Warrior / Rocío Martínez Pérez.   Children / Young Adults   Pg. 168
La Historia del Rey Transparente / Rosa Montero.   Literature / Fiction   Pg. 51
Historia del uno / María de la Luz Uribe.   Children / Young Adults   Pg. 160
Historia documental del cine mexicano / Emilio García Riera.   Reference   Pg. 152
Historia y crítica de la literatura española / Francisco Rico, ed.   Reference   Pg. 153
Historia y crítica de la literatura hispanoamericana / Cedomil Goic.   Reference   Pg. 153
Historias de clóset / Claudia Arcila.   Non fiction   Pg. 108
Historias de famas y cronopios / Julio Cortázar.   Literature / Fiction   Pg. 51
Historias de hadas para adultos / Daína Chaviano.   Literature / Fiction   Pg. 51
Historias de Verdad / Various.   Non fiction   Pg. 108
Las historias prohibidas del Pulgarcito / Roque Dalton.   Non fiction   Pg. 108
El hombre, la hembra y el hambre / Daína Chaviano.   Literature / Fiction   Pg. 51
La hormiga Miga... ¡liga! / Emili Teixidor.   Children / Young Adults   Pg. 176

I

Imán / Ramón J. Sender.   Literature / Fiction   Pg. 52

Incierta gloria / Joan Sales. · Literature / Fiction · Pg. 52
El Indio / Gregorio López y Fuentes. · Literature / Fiction · Pg. 52
Indios en rebelión / Néstor Taboada Terán. · Literature / Fiction · Pg. 52
Industrias y andanzas de Alfanhuí / Rafael Sánchez Ferlosio. · Literature / Fiction · Pg. 53
Inés del alma mía / Isabel Allende. · Literature / Fiction · Pg. 53
Las inquietudes de Shanti Andía / Pío Baroja. · Literature / Fiction · Pg. 53
La invención de Morel / Adolfo Bioy Casares. · Literature / Fiction · Pg. 53
Inventario I, II and III / Mario Benedetti. · Poetry / Drama · Pg. 131
El inventor de juegos / Pablo de Santis. · Children / Young Adults · Pg. 186
La Isla Bajo el Mar / Isabel Allende · Literature / Fiction · Pg. 54
La isla de los amores infinitos / Daína Chaviano · Literature / Fiction · Pg. 54
La isla que se repite / Antonio Benítez Rojo. · Non fiction · Pg. 109
La isla viajera / Antonio Orlando Rodríguez · Children / Young Adults · Pg. 168

▶ J K

Jorge Luis Borges / Georgina Lázaro. · Children / Young Adults · Pg. 177
José / Georgina Lázaro. · Children / Young Adults · Pg. 177
Juan Pérez Jolote: biografía de un tzotzil / Ricardo Pozas. · Non fiction · Pg. 109
Juana Inés / Georgina Lázaro. · Children / Young Adults · Pg. 177
El Juego del Angel / Carlos Ruiz Zafón. · Literature / Fiction · Pg. 54
El juguete rabioso / Roberto Arlt. · Literature / Fiction · Pg. 54
Julia / Georgina Lázaro. · Children / Young Adults · Pg. 177
Juventud en éxtasis / Carlos Cuauhtemoc Sánchez. · Literature / Fiction · Pg. 55

▶ L

La detective Julieta y el misterio de la clase / Carmen Gil Martínez. · Children / Young Adults · Pg. 165
La higuera / Ramiro Pinilla. · Literature / Fiction · Pg. 49
El laberinto de la soledad / Octavio Paz. · Literature / Fiction · Pg. 56
El laboratorio secreto / Lluís Prats Martínez; Enric Roig Tió. · Children / Young Adults · Pg. 186
El lápiz del carpintero / Manuel Rivas. · Literature / Fiction · Pg. 56
El largo viaje / Jorge Semprún. · Non fiction · Pg. 109
Latinoamérica: Su civilización y su cultura / Eugenio Chang Rodríguez. · Non fiction · Pg. 109
El Lazarillo de Tormes / Anonymous. · Literature / Fiction · Pg. 56
El lector novohispano / José Joaquín Blanco, ed. · Literature / Fiction · Pg. 57
Las lenguas de diamante / Juana de Ibarbourou. · Poetry / Drama · Pg. 132
Leo el dragón lector / José Andrés Villota Rocha. · Children / Young Adults · Pg. 168
Libro de buen amor / Juan Ruiz, Archipreste de Hita. · Poetry / Drama · Pg. 133
Libro de las preguntas / Pablo Neruda. · Children / Young Adults · Pg. 192
El libro de Nebal / Ma. del Carmen del Bosque Nieto. · Children / Young Adults · Pg. 178

Libro del Caballero Zifar / Anonymous	Literature / Fiction	Pg. 57
El libro del Conde Lucanor / Juan Manuel Infante de Castilla.	Literature / Fiction	Pg. 57
El libro del frío / Antonio Gamoneda.	Poetry / Drama	Pg. 131
El libro maldito de los templarios / Francisco Díaz Valladares.	Children / Young Adults	Pg. 187
Los libros arden mal / Manuel Rivas.	Literature / Fiction	Pg. 58
Literatura centroamericana: diccionario de autores centroamericanos: fuentes para su estudio / Jorge Eduardo Arellano.	Reference	Pg. 153
Literatura Puertorriqueña: Su proceso en el tiempo / Josefina Rivera de Alvarez.	Reference	Pg.153
La lluvia amarilla / Julio Llamazares.	Literature / Fiction	Pg. 58
Lo esencial en la ortografía / Francisco Alvero Frances.	Non fiction	Pg.110
Lo fugitivo permanece. 20 cuentos mexicanos / Carlos Monsiváis, ed.	Literature / Fiction	Pg. 58
Lo que está en mi corazón / Marcela Serrano.	Literature / Fiction	Pg. 58
Lo único que queda es el amor / Agustín Fernández Paz.	Children / Young Adults	Pg. 195
El loro de Robinson / Antonio A Gómez Yebra, .	Children / Young Adults	Pg. 160
Luces de bohemia / Ramón María del Valle Inclán.	Poetry / Drama	Pg. 133
Lucha Libre: The Man in the Silver Mask: A Bilingual Cuento / Xavier Garza.	Children / Young Adults	Pg. 178
Luis bandolero Luis / Walter Ventosilla.	Literature / Fiction	Pg. 59
Luna / Antonio Rubio y Oscar Villán.	Children / Young Adults	Pg. 168

M

Maddox descubre el camino / Care Santos Torres.	Children / Young Adults	Pg. 178
Mala onda / Alberto Fuguet.	Literature / Fiction	Pg. 59
Maldito amor / Rosario Ferré.	Literature / Fiction	Pg. 59
Malekin o el secreto del armario / Agustín Celis; Alejandra Ramírez.	Children / Young Adults	Pg. 178
Mamá elefante es genial / Gabriela Keselman.	Children / Young Adults	Pg. 161
La mano de Fátima / Ildefonso Falcones.	Literature / Fiction	Pg. 60
Las manos del pianista / Eugenio Fuentes.	Literature / Fiction	Pg. 60
Manual de traducción Inglés / Castellano / Gabriel López Guix, and J. Minnet Wilkinson.	Non fiction	Pg. 110
Mañana en la batalla, piensa en mi / Javier Marías.	Literature / Fiction	Pg. 60
Las maravillas de una sencilla sombrilla amarilla / Yanitzia Canetti; Ana López Escrivá.	Children / Young Adults	Pg. 179
Mares del sur / Noé Jitrik.	Literature / Fiction	Pg. 60
Margarita, está linda la mar / Sergio Ramírez.	Literature / Fiction	Pg. 61
La mariposa / Francisco Jiménez.	Children / Young Adults	Pg. 168
Martina y el mar / Paula Casal Rivas.	Children / Young Adults	Pg. 187
Más allá de mi / Francisco Jiménez.	Non fiction	Pg. 110
La más divertida historia de Mozart niño / Victoria Bermejo Sánchez Izquierdo.	Children / Young Adults	Pg. 169
Máscaras / Leonardo Padura.	Literature / Fiction	Pg. 61
Materia Prima: Protonovela / Marcio Veloz Maggiolo.	Literature / Fiction	Pg. 61
Me Gusta / Javier Sobrino, ilustradora Noemi Villamuza.	Children / Young Adults	Pg. 161
¿Me lo dejas? / Isabel Abedi.	Children / Young Adults	Pg. 161
Las medias de los flamencos / Horacio Quiroga.	Children / Young Adults	Pg. 161

El mejor es mi papá / Georgina Lázaro	Children / Young Adults	Pg. 169
Los mejores cuentos / Sergio Pitol	Literature / Fiction	Pg. 61
Melodrama / Jorge Franco.	Literature / Fiction	Pg. 62
Memoria de la melancolía / María Teresa León.	Non fiction	Pg. 110
Memorias de Altagracia / Salvador Garmendia.	Literature / Fiction	Pg. 62
Memorias de Mama Blanca / Teresa de la Parra	Literature / Fiction	Pg. 62
Memorias / Carlos Barral.	Non fiction	Pg. 111
Menguante / Alfredo Gómez Cerdá.	Children / Young Adults	Pg. 187
El mercado del libro antiguo español: una guía de precios / Julio Ollero, and Susana Bardón, eds.	Reference	Pg. 154
La merienda del señor Verde / Javier Sáez Castán.	Children / Young Adults	Pg. 179
México Ante Dios / Francisco Martín Moreno.	Literature / Fiction	Pg. 62
Mi caballo / Georgina Lázaro.	Children / Young Adults	Pg. 162
Mi vestido verde esmeralda / Alister Ramírez Márquez.	Literature / Fiction	Pg. 63
Milagros de Nuestra Señora / Gonzalo de Berceo.	Literature / Fiction	Pg. 63
Misión del bibliotecario y otros ensayos afines / José Ortega y Gasset.	Non fiction	Pg. 111
Miss Narco / Javier Valdéz Cárdenas.	Non fiction	Pg. 111
El misterio de la cripta embrujada / Eduardo Mendoza.	Literature / Fiction	Pg. 63
Misteriosa Buenos Aires / Manuel Mujica Lainez.	Literature / Fiction	Pg. 63
La mitad de tu rostro / Blanca Alvarez.	Children / Young Adults	Pg. 192
Mitología y artes prehispánicas de las Antillas / José Juan Arrom.	Non fiction	Pg. 112
Morris, quiero una pesadilla / Gabriela Keselman.	Children / Young Adults	Pg. 169
La muerte de Artemio Cruz / Carlos Fuentes.	Literature / Fiction	Pg. 64
La muerte y la doncella / Ariel Dorfman.	Literature / Fiction	Pg. 64
Muertos de papel / Alicia Giménez Bartlett.	Literature / Fiction	Pg. 64
La mujer del maestro / Guillermo Martínez.	Literature / Fiction	Pg. 55
Mujeres de ojos grandes / Angeles Mastretta.	Literature / Fiction	Pg. 64
Mujeres novelistas y novelas de mujeres en la posguerra española (1940-1965) / Raquel Conde Pen Alosa.	Reference	Pg. 154
El mundo / Juan José Millás.	Literature / Fiction	Pg. 65
El mundo alucinante / Reinaldo Arenas.	Literature / Fiction	Pg. 65
El mundo ha vivido equivocado / Roberto Fontanarrosa.	Literature / Fiction	Pg. 65
Los mundos que amo / Daína Chaviano.	Literature / Fiction	Pg. 65
Música de cine en España: Señas de identidad en la banda sonora contemporánea / Teresa Fraile Prieto.	Non fiction	Pg. 112
¡Muu, Moo!: Rimas de Animales / Ada Alma Flor & F. Isabel Campoy.	Children / Young Adults	Pg. 162

N Ñ

La nada cotidiana / Zoe Valdés.	Literature / Fiction	Pg. 66
Nada / Carmen Laforet.	Literature / Fiction	Pg. 66
Nadie encendía las lámparas / Felisberto Hernández.	Literature / Fiction	Pg. 66

Naiyakay: leyendas africanas / Severino Calleja Pérez.	Children / Young Adults	Pg. 179
Narraciones / Jorge Luis Borges.	Literature / Fiction	Pg. 66
Naufragios y Comentarios / Alvar Núñez Cabeza de Vaca.	Non fiction	Pg. 112
Niebla / Miguel de Unamuno.	Literature / Fiction	Pg. 66
Niña bonita / Ana María Machado.	Children / Young Adults	Pg. 179
No amanece el cantor / José Angel Valente.	Poetry / Drama	Pg. 133
No pasó nada / Antonio Skármeta.	Literature / Fiction	Pg. 67
No será la tierra / Jorge Volpi.	Literature / Fiction	Pg. 67
La noche de la reina Berenguela / Xosé Antonio Neira Cruz.	Children / Young Adults	Pg. 180
La Noche de los Lápices / María Seoane.	Non fiction	Pg. 113
La noche de Tlatelolco / Elena Poniatowska.	Non fiction	Pg. 113
La noche que Wendy aprendió a volar /Andreu Martín Farrero.	Children / Young Adults	Pg. 193
Nombre de torero / Luis Sepúlveda.	Literature / Fiction	Pg. 67
Noticias del Extranjero / Pedro Lastra.	Poetry / Drama	Pg. 134
La novela de mi vida / Leonardo Padura.	Literature / Fiction	Pg. 67
Novelas ejemplares / Miguel de Cervantes.	Literature / Fiction	Pg. 68
La novia de Odessa / Edgardo Cozarinsky.	Literature / Fiction	Pg. 68
La novia oscura / Laura Restrepo.	Literature / Fiction	Pg. 68
Nubosidad variable / Carmen Martín Gaite.	Literature / Fiction	Pg. 68
Nueva Enciclopedia de Puerto Rico / José A. Toro Sugrañés.	Reference	Pg. 154
Nueve novísimos poetas españoles / J.M. Castellet, selec.	Poetry / Drama	Pg. 134
Ñam / Puño	Children / Young Adults	Pg. 169

O

Obabakoak / Bernardo Atxaga.	Literature / Fiction	Pg. 69
Obra poética completa / Jorge Carrera Andrade.	Poetry / Drama	Pg. 134
Obra poética / Jorge Luis Borges.	Poetry / Drama	Pg. 135
Obra poética / Iñigo López de Mendoza Santillana, Marqués de.	Poetry / Drama	Pg. 135
Obras completas (y otros cuentos) / Augusto Monterroso.	Literature / Fiction	Pg. 69
Obras completas: Poesía completa y prosa selecta / Alejandra Pizarnik.	Poetry / Drama	Pg. 135
Obras escogidas / San Juan de la Cruz.	Poetry / Drama	Pg. 135
El obsceno pájaro de la noche / José Donoso.	Literature / Fiction	Pg. 69
Ochenta y seis cuentos / Quim Monzo.	Literature / Fiction	Pg. 69
Ojo por diente / Rubén Bareiro Saguier.	Literature / Fiction	Pg. 70
La ola Latina: cómo los hispanos están transformando la política en los Estados Unidos / Jorge Ramos.	Non fiction	Pg. 113
Olimpita / Hernán Migoya y Joan M. Marín.	Literature / Fiction	Pg. 70
Operación Masacre / Rodolfo Walsh.	Literature / Fiction	Pg. 70
Oráculo manual y arte de prudencia / Baltasar Gracián.	Non fiction	Pg. 113
Los orishas en Cuba / Natalia Bolívar Aróstegui.	Non fiction	Pg. 114
Ortografía de la lengua española / Edición revisada por las Academias de la Lengua Española.	Reference	Pg. 154

Ortografía y ortotipografía del español actual / José Martínez de Sousa.	Reference	Pg. 155
El oscurecer / Luis Mateo Díez.	Literature / Fiction	Pg. 71
Oscuro Bosque Oscuro / Jorge Volpi.	Literature / Fiction	Pg. 71
El oso cansado / Concha López Narváez; Rafael Salmerón López.	Children / Young Adults	Pg. 170
La otra mano de Lepanto / Carmen Boullosa.	Literature / Fiction	Pg. 71

P

Pablo / Georgina Lázaro.	Children / Young Adults	Pg. 180
Padre Rico, Padre Pobre / Robert T. Kiyosaki.	Non fiction	Pg. 114
El país bajo mi piel / Gioconda Belli.	Non fiction	Pg. 114
El país de cuatro pisos y otros ensayos / José Luis González.	Non fiction	Pg. 109
País de dragones / Daína Chaviano.	Children / Young Adults	Pg. 180
Palabra sobre palabra: obra completa (1956-2001) / Angel González.	Poetry / Drama	Pg. 136
Palabras cruzadas / Gabriel Rolón	Non fiction	Pg. 114
Pantaleón y las visitadoras / Mario Vargas Llosa.	Literature / Fiction	Pg. 71
Paradiso / José Lezama Lima.	Literature / Fiction	Pg. 72
Paraíso Travel / Jorge Franco.	Literature / Fiction	Pg. 72
La parranda / Eduardo Blanco Amor.	Literature / Fiction	Pg. 72
Los pasos del miedo / Concha López Narváez.	Children / Young Adults	Pg. 193
Los pasos perdidos / Alejo Carpentier.	Literature / Fiction	Pg. 72
Las patas del flamenco / Emma Romeu.	Children / Young Adults	Pg. 180
Paula / Isabel Allende.	Non fiction	Pg. 114
Los peces de la amargura / Fernando Aramburu.	Literature / Fiction	Pg. 73
Pedro Páramo / Juan Rulfo.	Literature / Fiction	Pg. 73
Pequeñas resistencias: antología del nuevo cuento español / Andrés Neuman, ed.	Literature / Fiction	Pg. 73
Percusión / José Balza.	Literature / Fiction	Pg. 74
El Persa. Ese desconocido / El Persa. José Cardona.	Children / Young Adults	Pg. 193
Persépolis / Marjane Satrapi.	Literature / Fiction	Pg. 74
Persona non grata / Jorge Edwards.	Non fiction	Pg. 115
Perspectivas culturales de Hispanoamérica / Juan Kattan Ibarra.	Non fiction	Pg. 115
Pétala / Pep Bruno Galán.	Children / Young Adults	Pg. 162
El pez en en el agua: memorias / Mario Vargas Llosa.	Non fiction	Pg. 105
Picasso para niños / Marina García Gurevich.	Children / Young Adults	Pg. 181
Pic-Nic. El triciclo. El laberinto / Fernando Arrabal.	Poetry / Drama	Pg. 136
Piedra de sol / Octavio Paz	Poetry / Drama	Pg. 136
La piel de toro / Salvador Espriu.	Poetry / Drama	Pg. 136
La piel fría / Albert Sánchez Piñol.	Literature / Fiction	Pg. 55
Plata quemada / Ricardo Piglia.	Literature / Fiction	Pg. 74
Platero y Yo (de Juan Ramón Jiménez contado a los niños) / Rosa Navarro Durán.	Children / Young Adults	Pg. 170
Platero y yo / Juan Ramón Jiménez.	Literature / Fiction	Pg. 74
La plaza del diamante / Mercè Rodoreda.	Literature / Fiction	Pg. 75

Plenilunio / Rogelio Sinán.	Literature / Fiction	Pg. 75
Pobre Manolito / Elvira Lindo.	Children / Young Adults	Pg. 187
Poemas clandestinos / Roque Dalton.	Poetry / Drama	Pg. 136
Poemas póstumos / Jaime Gil de Biedma.	Poetry / Drama	Pg. 137
Poesía varia / Francisco de Quevedo.	Poetry / Drama	Pg. 137
Poesía / Jorge Manrique.	Poetry / Drama	Pg. 137
Poesía / Ausiàs March.	Poetry / Drama	Pg. 138
Poesía / Fray Luis de León.	Poetry / Drama	Pg. 138
Poesías castellanas completas / Garcilaso de la Vega.	Poetry / Drama	Pg. 138
Poesías líricas / Lope de Vega.	Poetry / Drama	Pg. 138
Poesías / Luis de Góngora.	Poetry / Drama	Pg. 139
Poeta en Nueva York / Federico García Lorca.	Poetry / Drama	Pg. 139
Polisapo / Augusto Roa Bastos; Alejandro Maciel.	Children / Young Adults	Pg. 181
Pomelo se pregunta / Ramona Bâdescu.	Children / Young Adults	Pg. 162
Por donde sale el sol / Blanca Valdecasas.	Literature / Fiction	Pg. 75
Por el camino de Ulectra / Martín Casariego Córdoba.	Children / Young Adults	Pg. 188
Por el libro / Various.	Literature / Fiction	Pg. 76
Primavera con esquina rota / Mario Benedetti.	Literature / Fiction	Pg. 76
El primer nueva corónica y buen gobierno / Felipe Guaman Poma de Ayala.	Non fiction	Pg. 115
Las primeras representaciones gráficas del indio americano, 1493-1523 / Ricardo E. Alegría.	Non fiction	Pg. 115
Princesa va al teatro / Sagrario Pinto Martín.	Children / Young Adults	Pg. 170
El príncipe de la niebla / Carlos Ruiz Zafón.	Children / Young Adults	Pg. 194
Prosas profanas / Rubén Darío.	Poetry / Drama	Pg. 139
Pudor / Santiago Roncagliolo.	Literature / Fiction	Pg. 76

Q

Los que falsificaron la firma de Dios / Viriato Sención.	Literature / Fiction	Pg. 76
¿Qué se ama cuando se ama? / Gonzalo Rojas.	Poetry / Drama	Pg. 139
Querido enemigo / Agustín Fernández Paz.	Children / Young Adults	Pg. 181
¿Quién mató a Regiomontano? / Carlos Olalla Linares.	Children / Young Adults	Pg. 188
¿Quién se robó los colores? / Alister Ramírez Márquez.	Children / Young Adults	Pg. 181

R

Rayuela / Julio Cortázar.	Literature / Fiction	Pg. 77
La Raza Cómica: Del sujeto en Puerto Rico / Rubén Ríos Avila.	Non fiction	Pg. 116
Rebeca al bate y dos cuentos más / Dinorah Coronado.	Children / Young Adults	Pg. 181
La rebelión de las masas / José Ortega y Gasset.	Non fiction	Pg. 116
La rebelión de los arqueros / Jesús Ballaz Zabalza.	Children / Young Adults	Pg. 182

El recurso del Método / Alejo Carpentier. — Literature / Fiction — Pg. 77
La Regenta / Leopoldo Alas "Clarín". — Literature / Fiction — Pg. 77
La reina del sur / Arturo Pérez-Reverte. — Literature / Fiction — Pg. 78
La reina Isabel cantaba rancheras / Hernán Rivera Letelier. — Literature / Fiction — Pg. 78
El reinado de Witiza / Francisco García Pavón. — Literature / Fiction — Pg. 78
El reino de este mundo / Alejo Carpentier. — Literature / Fiction — Pg. 79
Relación acerca de las antigüedades de los indios / Ramón Pané, Fray, and José Juan Arrom, ed. — Non fiction — Pg. 116
Renaissance and Baroque Poetry of Spain / Elias L. Rivers. — Poetry / Drama — Pg. 139
Réquiem por un campesino español / Ramón J. Sender. — Literature / Fiction — Pg. 79
Residuos de los tiempos / Enrique Laguerre. — Poetry / Drama — Pg. 140
Respiración artificial / Ricardo Piglia. — Literature / Fiction — Pg. 79
Respuesta a Sor Filotea / Sor Juana Inés de la Cruz. — Non fiction — Pg. 117
Reunión de cuentos / Jesús Gardea. — Literature / Fiction — Pg. 79
El rey de las octavas / Emma Romeu. — Children / Young Adults — Pg. 182
Rimas y leyendas / Gustavo Adolfo Bécquer. — Poetry / Drama — Pg. 140
Los ríos profundos / José María Arguedas. — Literature / Fiction — Pg. 80
El rock de la momia y otros versos diversos / Antonio Orlando Rodríguez — Children / Young Adults — Pg. 182
Los rojos de ultramar / Jordi Soler. — Literature / Fiction — Pg. 80
Romancero Gitano / Federico García Lorca. — Poetry / Drama — Pg. 140
Rosario Tijeras / Jorge Franco. — Literature / Fiction — Pg. 80
El rufián moldavo / Edgardo Cozarinsky. — Literature / Fiction — Pg. 80

S

Sab / Gertrudis Gómez de Avellaneda. — Literature / Fiction — Pg. 81
La saga / fuga de J.B. / Gonzalo Torrente Ballester. — Literature / Fiction — Pg. 81
San Manuel Bueno Mártir / Miguel de Unamuno. — Literature / Fiction — Pg. 81
Santiago / Federico García Lorca. — Children / Young Adults — Pg. 188
El sapo distraído / Javier Rondón. — Children / Young Adults — Pg. 163
Semblanzas del corazón / José Rafael Lantigua. — Literature / Fiction — Pg. 81
El señor Presidente / Miguel Angel Asturias. — Literature / Fiction — Pg. 82
Serena / Juan Cruz Ruiz. — Children / Young Adults — Pg. 194
Si te dicen que caí / Juan Marsé. — Literature / Fictionn — Pg. 82
Las siete ciudades de Cíbola: textos y testimonios sobre la expedición Vázquez Coronado / Pedro de Castañeda Nájera, et al... — Non fiction — Pg. 117
Los siete hijos de Simenón / Ramón Díaz Eterovic. — Literature / Fiction — Pg. 82
Siete reporteros y un periódico / Pilar Lozano Carballo. — Children / Young Adults — Pg. 182
El siglo de las luces / Alejo Carpentier. — Literature / Fiction — Pg. 83
El siglo de Tintín / Fernando Castillo Cáceres. — Children / Young Adults — Pg. 194
El silencio / Horacio Veerbitsky. — Non fiction — Pg. 117
Sin ti no soy yo / Lourdes Vázquez. — Literature / Fiction — Pg. 83

Soldados de Salamina / Javier Cercas.	Literature / Fiction	Pg. 83
Soldados / Francisco González Ledesma.	Literature / Fiction	Pg. 83
Solitud / Víctor Català, pseud. de Caterina Albert.	Literature / Fiction	Pg. 84
Sólo cenizas hallarás (bolero) / Pedro Vergés.	Literature / Fiction	Pg. 84
Solo un muerto más / Ramiro Pinilla	Literature / Fiction	Pg. 84
La sombra de lo que fuimos / Luis Sepúlveda	Literature / Fiction	Pg. 84
La sombra del viento / Carlos Ruiz Zafón	Literature / Fiction	Pg. 85
Son de Mar / Manuel Vicent.	Literature / Fiction	Pg. 85
Sonetos / Luis de Góngora.	Poetry / Drama	Pg. 140
Sóngoro cosongo / Nicolás Guillén.	Poetry / Drama	Pg. 141
La sonrisa etrusca / José Luis Sampedro.	Literature / Fiction	Pg. 85
Soy campeón / Dinorah Coronado.	Literature / Fiction	Pg. 85
Soy el más guapo / Mario Ramos.	Children / Young Adults	Pg. 170
Los sueños de los hombres se los fuman las mujeres / Alister Ramírez Márquez.	Literature / Fiction	Pg. 85
Sueños y discursos / Francisco de Quevedo.	Literature / Fiction	Pg. 86
El Sur; seguido de Bene / Adelaida García Morales.	Literature / Fiction	Pg. 86
Sweet Dreams / Dulces Sueños / Pat Mora; illustrator: Maribel Suárez.	Children / Young Adults	Pg. 163
Del Ombligo de la Luna / Francisco Alarcón; illustrator: Maya Maribel Suárez.	Children / Young Adults	Pg. 171

Tala / Gabriela Mistral.	Poetry / Drama	Pg. 141
Tarde de invierno / Jorge Luján.	Children / Young Adults	Pg. 171
Te dí la vida entera / Zoé Valdés.	Literature / Fiction	Pg. 86
Teatro español de vanguardia / Agustín Muñoz-Alonso López, ed.	Poetry / Drama	Pg. 141
Teatro español: (de la A a la Z) / Javier Huerta Calvo; Emilio Peral Vega, and Héctor Urzáiz Tortajada.	Reference	Pg. 155
Tengo miedo torero / Pedro Lemebel.	Literature / Fiction	Pg. 86
Terrazo / Abelardo Díaz Alfaro.	Literature / Fiction	Pg. 87
Tesis de un homicidio / Diego Paszkowski.	Literature / Fiction	Pg. 87
Tesoros de la poesía en la lengua castellana / Regino García Badell.	Poetry / Drama	Pg. 141
El testigo / Juan Villoro.	Literature / Fiction	Pg. 87
The Firefly Spanish/English visual dictionary / Jean Claude Corbeil, and Ariane Archambault.	Reference	Pg. 155
La tía Julia y el escribidor / Mario Vargas Llosa.	Literature / Fiction	Pg. 87
El tiempo de los emperadores extraños / Ignacio del Valle.	Literature / Fiction	Pg. 88
Tino y la alfombra mágica / Antonio Valle.	Children / Young Adults	Pg. 171
El tío Bin Floren / Jesús Mari Olaizola Lazkano.	Children / Young Adults	Pg. 183
Tirant lo Blanc / Joanot Martorell.	Literature / Fiction	Pg. 88
Todos los cuentos / Cristina Fernández Cubas.	Literature / Fiction	Pg. 88
El Torito Negro / Antonio Ferres.	Children / Young Adults	Pg. 183
Traducción y traductología. Introducción a la traductología / Amparo Hurtado Albir.	Non fiction	Pg. 117
Traducción: literatura y literalidad / Octavio Paz.	Non fiction	Pg. 117

Tragicomedia mexicana: la vida en México de 1940 a 1970 / José Agustín.		Non fiction	Pg. 118
La travesía de Enrique / Sonia Nazario.		Non fiction	Pg. 118
Travesías / Jaime Salinas.		Non fiction	Pg. 118
Travesuras de la niña mala / Mario Vargas Llosa.		Literature / Fiction	Pg. 88
El tren pasa primero / Elena Poniatowska.	•	Literature / Fiction	Pg. 89
Tres amigos / Patxi Zubizarreta.		Children / Young Adults	Pg. 183
Tres tristes tigres / Guillermo Cabrera Infante.		Literature / Fiction	Pg. 89
Trilce / César Vallejo.		Poetry / Drama	Pg. 142
Trilogía sucia de La Habana / Pedro Juan Gutiérrez.		Literature / Fiction	Pg. 89
Tríptico del mal: Señas de identidad; Don Julián ; Juan sin tierra / Juan Goytisolo.		Literature / Fiction	Pg. 89
Triste, solitario y final / Osvaldo Soriano.		Literature / Fiction	Pg. 90
Tu rostro mañana / Javier Marías.		Literature / Fiction	Pg. 90
El túnel / Ernesto Sábato.		Literature / Fiction	Pg. 90
Tuntún de pasa y grifería / Luis Palés Matos.		Poetry / Drama	Pg. 142
Turandot / Giacomo Puccini; Joan de Déu Prats Pijoan.		Children / Young Adults	Pg. 195
Tuyo es el reino / Abilio Estévez.		Literature / Fiction	Pg. 90
La última escala del Tramp Steamer / Álvaro Mutis.		Literature / Fiction	Pg. 56
La última niebla / María Luisa Bombal.		Literature / Fiction	Pg. 91
La última noche de Dostoievski / Cristina Peri Rossi.		Literature / Fiction	Pg. 91
El último Catón / Matilde Asensi.		Literature / Fiction	Pg. 91

U

Un caballo de fuego / Fina Casalderrey.	Children / Young Adults	Pg. 172
Un mundo para Julius / Alfredo Bryce Echenique.	Literature / Fiction	Pg. 91
Un Puñado de Semillas / Monica Hughes Illustrations by Luis Garay.	Children / Young Adults	Pg. 183
Un regalo del cielo / Gustavo Martín Garzo.	Children / Young Adults	Pg. 172
Una palabra tuya / Elvira Lindo.	Literature / Fiction	Pg. 91
El unicornio / Manuel Mujica Lainez.	Literature / Fiction	Pg. 92

V W X

Veinte poemas de amor y una canción desesperada / Pablo Neruda.	Poetry / Drama	Pg. 142
Las venas abiertas de América Latina / Eduardo Galeano.	Non fiction	Pg. 118
La verdad sobre el caso Savolta / Eduardo Mendoza.	Literature / Fiction	Pg. 92
La verdad sospechosa / Juan Ruiz de Alarcón.	Literature / Fiction	Pg. 94
Versión Celeste / Juan Larrea.	Poetry / Drama	Pg. 142
Versos libres / José Martí.	Poetry / Drama	Pg. 142
El viaje de la evolución (El joven Darwin) / Vicente Muñoz Puelles.	Children / Young Adults	Pg. 188
Viajes al estrecho de Magallanes / Pedro Sarmiento de Gamboa.	Non fiction	Pg. 119
La vida del Buscón / Francisco de Quevedo.	Literature / Fiction	Pg. 92

La vida es sueño / Pedro Calderón de la Barca.	Poetry / Drama	Pg. 132
La vida exagerada de Martín Romaña / Alfredo Bryce Echenique.	Literature / Fiction	Pg. 92
Vida moderna hispana / James W. Brown.	Non fiction	Pg. 119
La vida perra de Juanita Narboni / Angel Vázquez.	Literature / Fiction	Pg. 93
El viento de la luna / Antonio Muñoz Molina.	Literature / Fiction	Pg. 93
Vikingos / Dolores Gassós.	Children / Young Adults	Pg. 184
Visión de Anáhuac y otros ensayos / Alfonso Reyes.	Non fiction	Pg. 119
Vivir para contarla / Gabriel García Márquez.	Non fiction	Pg. 120
La vorágine / José Eustaquio Rivera.	Literature / Fiction	Pg. 93
Vudú y magia en Santo Domingo / Carlos Esteban Deive.	Non fiction	Pg. 120
El vuelo de la reina / Tomás Eloy Martínez.	Literature / Fiction	Pg. 94
El vuelo de las cigüeñas / María Isabel Molina Llorente.	Children / Young Adults	Pg. 195
La vuelta al mundo en 80 páginas / Victoria Bermejo Sánchez Izquierdo.	Children / Young Adults	Pg. 184

Y Z

Ya está aquí ¡Don invierno! / Gabriel Segura Soler.	Children / Young Adults	Pg. 184
¡Ya llegan los Reyes Magos! / Georgina Lázaro.	Children / Young Adults	Pg. 172
Yo el supremo / Augusto Roa Bastos.	Literature / Fiction	Pg. 94
Yo me perdono / Fietta Jarque.	Literature / Fiction	Pg. 94
Yo, Naomi León / Pamela Muñoz Ryan.	Children / Young Adults	Pg. 184
Zara y el librero de Bagdag / Fernando Marías.	Children / Young Adults	Pg. 196

COLLABORATORS INDEX

A Z

Abreu, Sabrina	Instituto Cervantes New York
Acosta, Lucía	Princeton Public Library
Adams, Phyllis Y.	Virginia Beach City Public Schools
Agustí, Lluís	Instituto Cervantes New York
Alicea, Ismael	The New York Public Library
Alonso Regalado, Jesús	University of Albany
Alvarez, Mark	Salk Lake City Library
Aponte, Sarah	Dominican Studies Institute. CUNY
Ayala, Marcelo	Instituto Cervantes Chicago
Berdaner, Daniel	Forest Hill Public Library
Berman, Martha	Professor of Language and Literature
Bibel, Barbara	Oakland Public Library
Block, David	Cornell University
Cabanas, Santiago	Cónsul General de España en Miami
Canó, Pedro	Instituto Cervantes New York
Carbajal, Paloma Celis	UW-Madison
Casado, María	Miami Dade College
Chapa, Teresa	University of North Carolina at Chapel Hill
Chapa Domercq, Mónica	Oceanside Public Library
Chavarría, Alma	Houston Public Library
Conget, José María	Writer
Corrigan, Martin	Houston Public Library
Cuesta, Patricia	Los Angeles Public Library
Debesis, Juan Pablo	Lectorum
Dedéu, Bernat	Cadena Ser
Eagan, Cynthia	Detroit Public Library - Conely Branch
Encinas, Angela	San Bernardino Public Library
Fewell, Rachel	Anythink Libraries
Figueroa, Patricia	Brown University
Flores Correa, Mónica	Professor and Writer
Fundación Germán Sánchez Ruipérez, SOL	Fundación Germán Sánchez Ruipérez, SOL
García, Elizabeth	Queens Library
García, Marshall	Dominican University, Chicago
García Canido, Xosé Luis	Instituto Cervantes
García, Maripaz	Yale University
Gentle, María E.	Arlington Public Library
Gil de Cwilich, Silvia	Artist and Reader
Graciani, Paloma	Biblioteca "José Emilio Pacheco"
Griego, Adan	Stanford University Libraries
Hernández Piché, Bruno	Mexican Writer and Diplomat
Heyer, Richard	Instituto Cervantes New York
Hicks, Alison	University Colorado
Hurtado Gracia, Angélica	LAPL
Jennifer Battle, Dr.	Texas State University-San Marcos
Klasterka, Nancy	Hoover Public Library
Kozakowski, Enriqueta	Detroit Public Library - Bowen Branch
Lago, Eduardo	Instituto Cervantes New York
Lamadrid, Eduardo de	Trans-Lingual Communications Inc.
Langer de Ramírez, Lori	Herricks Public Schools, NY
Larson, Jeffry	Yale University Library

La Salle, Tom	Ferguson Library
Lerner, Isaías	CUNY
Lindo, Elvira	Writer and Journalist
Lizarraga, Yeni	Adler's Foreign Books INC.
Lord, Sherry	Claremont Inmersión in Arlington
Luna, Alfons	AFP New York
Mansilla, Diego	Acton-Boxborough Regional High School
Marcano, Nashieli	University of Akron
Martí Olivella, Jaume	University of New Hampshire
Martín, Ellen H.	Southampton Intermediate School
Martínez, Sara	Tulsa City-County Library
Medina Ortiz, Norma	Seminole County Public Library System
Medlar, Andrew	Chicago Public Library
Miletich, Marko	Binghamton University (SUNY)
Mlawer, Teresa	Lectorum Publications
Mulkay, Nellie B.	New York State Spanish Bilingual Education Technical Assistance Center at NYU
Núñez, Octavio	US Librarian
Orozco, Gaspar	Mexican Poet and Diplomat
Ortega, Alma	University of San Diego
Partlow, Gabriel	Pima County Public Library
Pendleton, Mark	Branigan Library Las Cruces NM
Pérez Mercado, Rafael	Biblioteca Pública Raquel Quiñones
Pérez Zúñiga, Ernesto	Instituto Cervantes
Peterson, Christine	Marantha Academy
Potts, Claude	University of California
Puig, Rita Aurora	Arapahoe Library District
Raffo Magnasco, Guillermina	St. Thomas University
Ramos, Marisol	Universidad de Connecticut
Reforma	Reforma
Rex, Mark	Salt Lake City Public Library
Riestra, Blanca	Instituto Cervantes Albuquerque
Rivas, Julio	Reader
Rodríguez, Miriam	Dallas Public Library
Romano, Natalie	Colorado Supreme Court Law Library
Romero, Libbhy	Brooklyn Public Library
San Juan, Alina	Trade Comission of Spain
Sanabria, Alvaro	San Francisco Public Library
Santiago Cervantes, Angel	Cahesa
Shirey, Lynn	Harvard College Library
Suárez, Radamés	Queens Library
Tarrago, Rafael E.	University of Minnesota
Torrance, Millie	Sacramento Public Library
Trapote Igneri, Odalys	New York City Department of Education
Valladares, Miguel	Dartmouth College
Van Jacob, Scott	University of Notre Dame
Vargas, Luis Francisco	Yuma County Library District
Velázquez Medina, Fernando	Writer and Journalist
Vergara, Salvador	Instituto Cervantes Chicago
Vidal, Juan Carlos	Instituto Cervantes Chicago
Villamar, Marlenys	Professor
Weiss, Stephanie	University of North Florida Library
Wenzel, Sarah G.	University of Chicago
Zaman, Robert	US Librarian
Zulueta, Carmen de	Writer and Professor

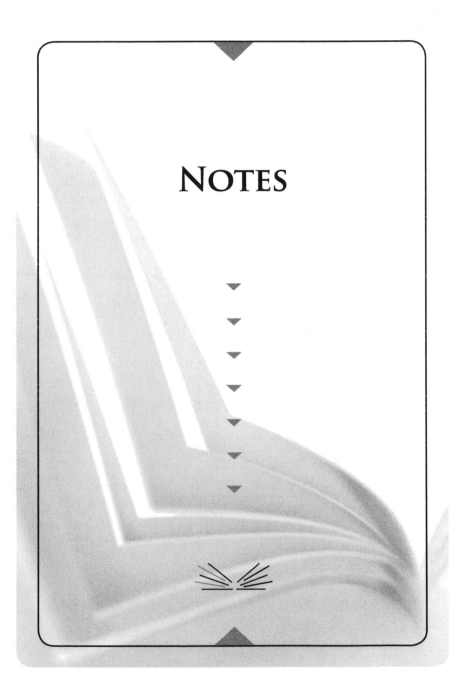

NOTES

NOTES

NOTES

NOTES

NOTES

NOTES

NOTES

NOTES

NOTES

NOTES

NOTES

NOTES

NOTES

NOTES